IT'S A FUNNY OLD WORLD

MORE SHORT PLAYS FOR LARGE CASTS
BILL TORDOFF

Heinemann Educational
a division of Heinemann Educational Books Ltd
Halley Court, Jordan hill, Oxford OX2 8EJ
OXFORD   LONDON   EDINBURGH
MADRID   ATHENS   BOLOGNA   PARIS
MELBOURNE   SYDNEY   AUCKLAND   SINGAPORE
TOKYO   IBADAN   NAIROBI   HARARE   GABORONE
PORTSMOUTH   NH   (USA)

Copyright © Bill Tordoff 1991
First published 1991

ISBN 0 435 23903 1

CAUTION

Typeset by Cambridge Composing (UK) Ltd
Printed and bound in Great Britain by
Richard Clay Ltd, Bungay, Suffolk

CONTENTS

INTRODUCTION

The plays in this collection were all written to give a whole mixed class the chance to read or put on a play together. Although some parts are larger than others, they are all characters with individual speeches as well as lines spoken or sung as members of a group.

All four plays are set in fantasy worlds. Soap salesmen weren't around 1,000 years ago, for instance, and the planet Neptune of *It's A Funny Old World* is not a real planet, but a variation on the Mars created by Ray Bradbury in *The Martian Chronicles*. The plays glance at various topics including advertising, authority, law and order, politics, religion, royalty, war and women's rights, but although they could be used as starting-points for discussion, they're intended mainly to entertain.

Readings

If you're going to read a play as a group, it's useful to look through your part beforehand, both to get some idea of the character and in case there are any lines or words that aren't clear. (Note also all the lines labelled ALL, WOMEN, ADULTS, etc, which are spoken by your group.)

It's helpful to have someone who will read in a line if the reading is held up because someone has lost his/her place: nothing kills a reading more surely than repeated stoppages. If you mispronounce or omit a word, it's usually better to keep the play going than stop to go back or apologise. There should normally be no pause at all between the end of one speech and the beginning of the next: it's sometimes better if they overlap slightly. And always attack your lines, speaking them with character and feeling.

NOTES FOR NOVICE DIRECTORS

Preparation

If you're going to perform a play before an audience, write to the publisher for permission. Then feel free to change it to suit your cast, for instance by increasing or decreasing the number of parts by re-allocating the lines. Once you've cast it, make sure your actors know what sort of character they're playing. (You can discuss this after the first read-through.)

One of the main problems of staging a large-cast play is to group your characters in a varied and interesting way and so that they can be seen both by the audience and other actors who speak to them. You need to plan moves and groupings before you start rehearsals, even if you have to modify them later.

Early rehearsals

Take your cast through all the moves, making sure that they pencil them in their scripts.

Remind them that acting consists not just in saying lines but in remaining in part throughout. Where a large number of actors are on stage, only a few will be speaking at any given time. The others will not go far wrong if they look at the speakers, their faces showing their reactions.

Speeches allocated in the script to a group can be broken up and spoken by different actors. In this case, it helps to draw the audience's attention if each individual moves slightly before speaking.

Learning a part

The cast should learn their parts only when they know how to say their lines and when to move. They need to learn the part as they are going to perform it, speaking clearly and with feeling, on cue and with the appropriate moves. (And not only their own individual lines, but also those spoken or sung by their group.)

Later rehearsals

Throughout rehearsals, your actors should speak as loudly as in performance. You can monitor audibility by conducting later rehearsals from the back of the room.

Once the scripts are put down, rehearsals should begin to approximate to performance. Practise going straight from one scene to another, striking (taking down or off) and setting (putting up or bringing on) scenery and props very quickly. If the production is to go smoothly, it is vital that properties (or substitutes) are used in rehearsals: actors need constant practice both to remember lines and to cope with props such as the soap packets and the thunder-sheet in *Soft Soap*, the guns and flags in *It's A Funny Old World*, the bottles in *Sell Out*, and the masks in *Castle Royal*.

Above all, keep reminding yourself that despite the inevitable difficulties and frustrations in rehearsals, it's all worthwhile. There are few feelings more pleasant for director and actors than the elation (and relief!) when the cast take their final curtain call.

B.T.

It's A Funny Old World

CHARACTERS

CISSIE
DOTTY
MOLLY
AUGUSTA (GUS)
EDWINA (EDDIE)
KITTY
GEORGINA (GEORGE)
TERESA (TERRY)
PEGGY
POLLY

The First Mission
SPACE 1, *the Captain*
SPACE 2, *the Lieutenant*
SPACE 3
SPACE 4
SPACE 5, *the radioman*

The Second Mission
SPACE 6, *The Captain*
SPACE 7, *the Lieutenant*
SPACE 8
SPACE 9, *the radioman*
SPACE 10, *the Reader*

SCENE: The Paradise Club
TIME: The near future

Costume The girls all wear Edwardian costume, more or less: floor-length, flared skirts and high-necked blouses with long leg-of-mutton sleeves.

All the Spacemen should wear similar silver space-suits. Otherwise, each Mission can wear track-suits or boiler-suits of their own colour. The second Mission do not need helmets, and it would be useful if the members of the first Mission had a clip to fasten their helmets to their belt or pack. Members of each Mission all wear a large Mission badge with the same symbol as their flag (see below).

All carry packs, the two Captains' being the smallest and the Lieutenants' being able to hold a (stiffened) flag on a telescopic or folding pole. The other six all carry large packs, with a long aerial protruding from each radioman's.

SPACE 6 and SPACE 10 wear spectacles.

The Captains each wear a pistol in a holster; all the others carry short automatic rifles with slings.

The FLAGS should be quite different in colour and design, and should not resemble existing national flags. The main feature of the U.S.E. flag could be a simplified map of Europe, while the Chettleite flag might be a black book (with the initials Z.C.) on a white ground. (Their insignia should not include a cross or other identifiable religious symbol.) The flag-poles should ideally have their own stand, perhaps based on folding music-stands. Otherwise, there can be a socket on the stage or on the corner of the pavilion.

The Play

The front of the pavilion of the Paradise Club. One door (open) leads into the bar and the changing-rooms. Another, closed, door is labelled STORE. On the verandah are tables and chairs. A few steps lead down. The atmosphere is relaxed and summery. CISSIE is sketching DOTTY, who is posed near the top of the steps. MOLLY is reading. There is a ripple of clapping from offstage, and DOTTY joins in.

CISSIE: Keep still, Dotty.

DOTTY: Gus made a splendid shot. Absolutely topping. Did you see it, Molly?

MOLLY: No. Cricket bores me to death.

DOTTY: Well, don't tell them: they live for it.

A loud 'Howzat!' from offstage, then applause.

DOTTY: Out at last!

AUGUSTA enters from the wings carrying an old cricket-bat.

DOTTY: Well done, Gus! How many?

AUGUSTA: Two hundred and eighty nine.

DOTTY: Better luck next time.

EDWINA appears from the pavilion. AUGUSTA gives her the bat.

AUGUSTA: Watch out for George's lobs, Eddie.

EDWINA: Huh! Watch me slog 'em!

EDWINA walks into the wings to a spatter of applause.

AUGUSTA (*looking at the drawing*): Who on earth's that?

DOTTY: Me, you dim-wit!

AUGUSTA (*looking from the picture to DOTTY*): Of course it is! Just like you: absolutely ripping! I must have a drink.

AUGUSTA goes into the pavilion. KITTY comes out with a tin and a tin-opener.

KITTY: This blasted tin!

CISSIE ⎫
DOTTY ⎬ : Ssh! Temper!
MOLLY ⎭

KITTY: I don't care!

MOLLY: You'll care if you swear. Give it to me. What's in it?

KITTY: Textured vegetable protein.

CISSIE: What on earth's that?

KITTY: Haven't the faintest. It's all we have: I hope another ship comes soon. (*Looking at the picture*) Who's that?

DOTTY: Me.

KITTY: Just like you! Super! Aren't you clever, Cissie?

MOLLY (*giving her the tin, opened*): There you are, my dear.

KITTY: Oh, thanks. We'll be eating soon. I suppose you can serve this stuff raw?

MOLLY: I suppose so.

KITTY *goes inside.*

DOTTY: Eddie's going to be out next ball.

CISSIE: How do you know?

'How.zat!' *offstage and applause.*

DOTTY: See? Here comes Eddie: absolutely furious.

EDWINA *marches in from the wings.*

EDWINA: That umpire wasn't even looking! Picking a flower!

CISSIE ⎫
DOTTY ⎬ : Don't swear!

EDWINA (*throwing the bat down*): Damn!

There is a sharp bang. EDWINA *screams and holds her head.*

AUGUSTA (*appearing with a drink*): Who swore?

MOLLY: Eddie.

AUGUSTA: Was it the umpire? (EDWINA *nods*) She's sweet, really. Drink this.

EDWINA: You'd think I'd have learned to keep my temper with her after all these years.

MOLLY: At least you've never tried to shoot her.

KITTY (*appearing in the doorway*): Lunch! Are we all here?

AUGUSTA: George and Terry are fielding. (*Waving into the wings*) They've seen us.

KITTY: Where are Peggy and Poppy?

CISSIE: Gone to the hut to switch on the Marconi beacon.

DOTTY (*scornful*): 'Marconi'! They say 'radio' nowadays. 'Marconi' is old hat.

CISSIE: Well, we are old, aren't we?

DOTTY: No! We're as young as we ever were.

MOLLY: Here come George and Terry.

Enter GEORGINA *and* TERESA *from the wings.*

MOLLY: Who won, Georgina?

GEORGINA: We did.

MOLLY: And who was the Woman of the Match, Teresa?

TERESA: Me.

AUGUSTA: Who says?

TERESA: Me.

Laughter. KITTY *appears in the doorway.*

KITTY: Lunch! Textured vegetable protein and dried yogurt.

ALL. Ugh!

KITTY: Don't blame me. Serve yourselves.

They start going inside the pavilion.

GEORGINA: I could eat a horse. Do you remember horses?

TERESA: Of course I do. My father and brothers played polo.

GEORGINA: Mine had a coal business.

TERESA: I'd forgotten about coal. Fancy, having to heat buildings!

GEORGINA: Peggy and Poppy.

PEGGY *and* POPPY *run in.*

PEGGY: Is lunch ready?

TERESA: Serve yourself: it sounds disgusting. Is the beacon working?

POPPY: Yes: we've switched it to S.O.S.

AUGUSTA (*appearing, cheerful*): That stuff is totally revolting. I refuse to touch it. (*To* PEGGY *and* POPPY) Any ships answering the beacon?

PEGGY ⎫
POPPY ⎭ : We could hear two talking.

AUGUSTA: Two! Where from?

> *During the following,* GEORGINA, TERESA *and* PEGGY *go inside, and gradually* ALL *come out, some with dishes.* PEGGY *brings a plate for* POPPY.

PEGGY: We're not sure, because they all speak English.

POPPY: I think the nearer one's from the U.S.E.

AUGUSTA: You mean U.S.A., dear.

POPPY: No, U.S.E.: United States of Europe. The Americans aren't united any more.

AUGUSTA: Fancy that! Where's the other ship from?

POPPY: We think that's American.

AUGUSTA: Oh, no! Not Space Coke and cubed hamburgers again!

POPPY: Well, the European food should be tastier.

EDWINA (*appearing*): All men on these ships, are they, Poppy?

POPPY: Aren't they always?

EDWINA: I keep dreaming of a really fast bowler turning up.

GEORGINA: He'd use a hard ball, and that 'ud finish you.

EDWINA: And him.

> ALL *laugh.*

MOLLY: Men!

ALL (*smiling*): Men!

> *Offstage, the whistle of a descending rocket.* ALL *turn to watch it, smiling gently.*

PEGGY: Here she comes: Rocket-ship Number Eleven.
TERESA: Well done, Poppy and Peggy!
KITTY: Pass me your dishes and I'll stick them in the water.

The dishes are passed to KITTY, who goes inside.

DOTTY: Are you going to draw them, Cissie?
CISSIE: No, they all look alike.
PEGGY: Their badges are different.
MOLLY: And their flags!
GEORGINA: Their flags!

ALL *are convulsed with laughter.* KITTY *appears with a dish-cloth.*

KITTY: What's funny?
MOLLY: Flags!
KITTY (*bursting into laughter*): Flags!

KITTY *goes back inside.*

DOTTY: Shh! Here they come!

ALL *try to bottle up their laughter and look dignified.* SPACE 1 *enters warily downstage on the opposite side, glances round without registering the* GIRLS, *beckons into the wings, realises what he's seen and turns his head slowly to stare at the* GIRLS *as the rest of* MISSION ONE *appear. They also stop and stare.* ALL *wear space-suits and carry guns at the ready. (See introductory note on costume and kit.) The* GIRLS, *still smiling, give a little wave.* SPACE 1 *beckons* DOTTY.

DOTTY: Me?

He nods. She looks at the other GIRLS, *shrugs and crosses. He beckons her closer and, gesturing round, says something, inaudible because of his helmet.*

DOTTY: You'll have to shout, dear! (*He shouts.* DOTTY *turns to the other* GIRLS) He says 'Is the air safe to breathe?'

The GIRLS nod encouragingly. SPACE 1 removes his helmet. The GIRLS clap politely. He breathes deeply and gives a thumbs-up to the other MEN, who also remove their helmets. The GIRLS clap again.

DOTTY: Welcome to Neptune. Did you have a good journey?
MEN (*bewildered*): Yes.
KITTY (*coming out, startled*): Oh!

The MEN whirl round, guns aimed.

DOTTY: Don't shoot: you'll hurt yourselves! Visitors, Kitty.
KITTY: Have they eaten?
DOTTY: Have you eaten?
SPACE 2: No, mam'selle, we haven't eaten.
GIRLS (*delighted, half-mocking*): Mam'selle!
TERESA: We've just had lunch. Haven't we, girls?
GIRLS: Mmm.
SPACE 1: Well, if there's any to spare . . .
SPACE 3: What did you have?
KITTY: Erm . . .
POPPY: Omelette.
KITTY: Omelette.
SPACE 4: Hey, you must have hens here!
MOLLY: Aren't you clever to guess that?
SPACE 4: I don't see them around.
MOLLY (*looking*): No, they must have . . .
PEGGY: Flown.
MOLLY: Flown.
KITTY: I'll see what I can rustle up. Any more to come?
SPACE 1: No, we're the whole crew. You men can put your packs down. (SPACE 3 & 4 *do so with groans of relief. To* SPACE 5) You as well.
SPACE 5: Sir, you told me never to . . .
SPACE 1: I'm telling you now! We're safe: can't you see?

SPACE 5 *shrugs and removes his pack.*

SPACE 1 (*looking round in amazement*): I simply can't believe all this!

DOTTY: You mean, about the hens?

SPACE 1: No, everything. We were on our way to explore Neptune, but with strict orders not to land, then we pick up S.O.S. signals from somewhere on the surface. Right?

SPACE 5: That's right, sir.

SPACE 1: We were amazed to hear signals, because over the last twenty years, ten missions have left Earth for this planet, and not one has returned. The signals from each one have ceased soon after arrival: just like that. Right, men?

MEN: Right, sir!

SPACE 1: So we land, but there's no other rocket. Just plains of blue grass, clumps of trees, streams, and this . . .

SPACE 2: Does it have a name, this, er . . . park?

MOLLY: Yes, Paradise.

SPACE 3: Paradise! You mean, we're dead?

MOLLY: Oh, good heavens: not yet, no.

DOTTY: Of course you're not dead!

GIRLS: No!

SPACE 2: And dare I say that you ladies look, er, lively?

GIRLS: Oh, we are!

SPACE 2: Well, how about giving us a tour?

DOTTY: Why not? Ladies, show the gentlemen around!

The GIRLS rise, chattering and smiling, and the MEN move towards them.

SPACE 1: Who told you men to move?

ALL freeze.

SPACE 2: Sir, I thought . . .

SPACE 1: I do the thinking, Lieutenant! You're still on duty! Line the men up!

SPACE 2: Spacemen! Form threes!

The three OTHER RANKS *stand in line, shuffling to get exactly aligned.*

SPACE 2: Attention! (*To* SPACE 1, *saluting*) Men formed in threes, sir!

GEORGINA: They're very smart!

GIRLS: Mmm.

EDWINA: I fancy the Lieutenant as a fast bowler.

TERESA: I just fancy him.

The GIRLS *laugh.*

SPACE 1: Stand easy! (*To* DOTTY) Ma'am, could I ask you some questions about this place?

DOTTY: But of course! We're all at your service, aren't we, girls?

GIRLS: Absolutely!

SPACE 1: I don't know where to begin . . .

DOTTY: Begin at the beginning, and go on till you come to the end.

MOLLY: Then stop. 'Alice'.

SPACE 1: Sorry?

DOTTY: What do you want to know, Captain?

SPACE 1: Well, for a start, how do you all come to be here, on Neptune?

CISSIE: We came on a rocket-ship, like everybody else.

SPACE 2: But there were no women astronauts on any of the Neptune ships in the last twenty years.

POPPY: Ah, but we came on the first space rocket.

PEGGY: In 1913.

SPACE 1: *Nineteen thirteen*??

POPPY: That's right. To escape the coming war.

SPACE 4: Sir! Yuri Gagarin was put into space in 1961 by the first space rocket! Every astronaut knows that, sir!

MEN: Right! 1961: first man in space! First space rocket!

GIRLS: Second.

SPACE 1: That's impossible!

POPPY: It may be impossible, but it's true.

PEGGY: Rockets have been around a long time.

MOLLY: Jules Verne and H. G. Wells foresaw it all.

SPACE 3: Aw! They were just writers.

SPACE 5: But Arthur C. Clarke was just a writer, and he invented satellites.

SPACE 2: I think it's possible, sir. I mean, back in 1913 they were building enormous ocean liners and giant airships. Why not a rocket?

GIRLS: Why not?

SPACE 1: I'll tell you why not: because if you girls came here as part of a rocket crew in 1913, you must all be a hundred years old!

SPACE 2 (*shocked*): Sir!

GIRLS (*shocked*): Oh! (*They click their tongues in disapproval*)

KITTY: Oh, that's a terrible thing to say!

She bursts into tears and other GIRLS comfort her.

DOTTY: Captain, I took you for a gentleman, but to blunder in here uninvited and to insult these innocent young ladies with coarse aspersions about their age is the action of a cad and a boor!

GIRLS: Hear, hear!

SPACE 2: You've got to apologise, sir!

SPACE 1: I'm very sorry: it must be the journey. Nothing makes sense any more.

PEGGY: Captain, do you know that this planet takes 165 Earth years to go round the sun? We've been here for less than one Neptunian year.

SPACE 1: Yes: so?

POPPY: Think about it.

SPACE 1: I will. Perhaps your menfolk can explain it to us.

DOTTY: Who?

SPACE 1: Your menfolk. I suppose they're around. (*Looking at the GIRLS, who smile enigmatically*) Aren't they?

GIRLS (*shaking their heads, smiling*): No-o!

SPACE 2: Are you trying to tell us that you women made a rocket
   and flew here on your own?

GIRLS (*tantalising*): Er . . . No!

SPACE 1 (*angry*): Then where are your men?

GIRLS (*fingers to lips*): Shh!

GEORGINA: Don't shout!

SPACE 1 (*shouting*): I'll shout if I want, dammit!

GIRLS (*apprehensive, putting their hands over their ears*): Ooh!

   The loud crack is heard again. SPACE 1 *yells and clasps his head.*
   The MEN *grab their guns and crouch facing out, ready to fire.*

SPACE 1 (*quietly*): Can you see anyone, men?

SPACE 5: No, sir.

SPACE 4: Nothing moving, sir.

SPACE 3: There's nothing, sir.

SPACE 1: Relax. (*To* DOTTY) What was that?

DOTTY (*to* PEGGY *and* POPPY): Come and tell him.

PEGGY (*coming forward with* POPPY): It's to do with thought-
   waves.

POPPY: We calmed Kitty down just now by loving thoughts,
   right?

SPACE 1. Yes.

PEGGY: There are different kinds of thought-waves. Some are
   powerful, like you make your men obey you by using the
   power of your mind.

SPACE 1 (*half-convinced*): Yes, but . . .

POPPY: Shh! Listen!

PEGGY: And some waves are positive and some are negative. On
   this planet, positive forces are exodotic.

SPACE 4: What?

POPPY: Positive thoughts go out from you. Like radio waves:
   Marconi waves.

SPACE 5: We know what a radio wave is! But what hurt the
   Captain?

POPPY: Tell him the rule about negative waves on Neptune,
   girls!

GIRLS: Negative waves are reciprocal!

SPACE 5: What?

DOTTY: Negative waves are reciprocal.

SPACE 3: Sir, have we travelled five billion kilometers to hear this twaddle? When do we eat?

KITTY: Soon.

SPACE 1: Good. We must return to the ship and send back a report.

GIRLS (*disappointed*): Oh, dear!

SPACE 1: So, quickly, what does 'Negative waves are reciprocal' mean?

GEORGINA: It means this: if you swear, or shout at someone, or even hate them strongly enough, you are giving out negative waves, and on Neptune negative waves bounce back to you. So do bullets. Any harmful energy is returned to the sender. Our menfolk found that out before they died.

TERESA: Or as they died.

SPACE 1: So when I cursed, I cursed myself?

GIRLS: By Jove, he's got it!

SPACE 2: That seems an easy lesson for a man to remember.

TERESA: If you do remember it, you'll be the first men who have.

SPACE 2: No cussing and swearing round here!

MEN: No, sir!

SPACE 2: But loving's in order: all right, sir?

SPACE 1: Well, er, yes!

SPACE 2: Loving's in order, men!

MEN: Yes, sir!

SPACE 1: Are you telling me that all your men died because they thought negative thoughts?

AUGUSTA: You're thinking negative thoughts now! Let's be positive! What food do you have in your ship?

GIRLS: Yes! Food!

SPACE 1: Food! I'm glad you asked! This mission marks a breakthrough in space catering. Tell them, Number 3!

SPACE 3: Willingly, sir. (*He has made this speech many times before*)

As well as carrying standard packs of condensed and dehydrated food, our rocket is the first to boast a fully-equipped kitchen. And as this crew comes from all over the United States . . .

EDWINA: Of Europe?

SPACE 3: Of course. Each man was allowed to choose his own menus for the flight. They can tell you themselves what they're looking forward to eating this evening. For instance, my chosen dishes include marinated courgettes and Italian chocolate cream cake.

GIRLS (*ecstatic*): Oh! (*As each man recites his menu, the GIRLS give little sighs and moans*)

SPACE 2: Mine are lamb with chestnuts followed by almond and pine-nut pastry.

GIRLS: Oh!!

SPACE 4: I chose a simple Greek meat stew, with rabbit marinaded in red wine, followed by walnut cake.

GIRLS: Oh!

SPACE 5: Me, I have chosen green beans with ham, followed by a salad with citrus, almond and honey.

GIRLS: Ahh!

SPACE 1: And for me, it just had to be a good old roast beef and two veg followed by jam roly-poly with lashings of custard!

GIRLS: Oh, divine!

SPACE 1: Why do you ask?

AUGUSTA: Just idle curiosity.

SPACE 1: Oh. First, we must take possession of this planet on behalf of the U.S.E. See what the Lieutenant has in his pack!

SPACE 2 *extracts the European flag, pole and stand, and sets it up while the GIRLS show their appreciation.*

AUGUSTA: It's a flag-pole!

EDWINA: How clever!

GEORGINA: Whatever will they think of next!

CISSIE: What a pretty flag! Is it a new design?

SPACE 3: It's the brand new European flag. The first time in space.

CISSIE: How killing!

The flag is now flying. SPACE 4 has produced a transistor player which he switches on. The MEN salute the flag while it plays a section of the Ode to Joy from Beethoven's Choral Symphony. Hesitantly the GIRLS rise. When they think it has finished they start to sit, then hurriedly rise as it plays another verse.

SPACE 1: I formally take possession of this planet on behalf of the United States of Europe.

DOTTY: I'm afraid that nobody owns anything or anybody on Neptune, Captain.

SPACE 1: That's going to change. Tomorrow we shall set up a monetary system, a legal system, and a system of military service. We shall also draw up the rules of the road and open a Stock Market.

MEN: Rah, rah, rah!

SPACE 2: Could I make a suggestion, sir? We've travelled through space for years to get here. Don't you think we deserve a holiday before we start work? After all, here we are in Paradise with unlimited sporting facilities and ten pretty ladies to look after us.

SPACE 1: But when we go back . . .

SPACE 4: Sir! We don't have to go back, sir.

SPACE 3: It's a long, dangerous flight, sir.

SPACE 5: And if we stay here we'll live for ever.

SPACE 2: Right! Who wants to go back?

The MEN look at each other.

SPACE 1 (*thinks, then, to* SPACE 5): Are we transmitting now?

SPACE 5: Yes, sir. Our call-sign is going out on automatic from this radio.

SPACE 1: But not from the ship?

SPACE 5: No, sir.

SPACE 1: Switch it off.

SPACE 5 (*reaches out to switch it off, then hesitating*): Sir, if I switch it off, Mission Control on Earth will think we're dead like all the others.

SPACE 1: Who wants to stay?

One after another, the MEN *raise their hands.*

SPACE 1: Right, kill the call-sign.

SPACE 5 hesitates for a moment, then turns a switch and throws the set into the wings.

SPACE 5: We're cut off now, sir.

The GIRLS *give a long sigh of satisfaction.*

SPACE 2: Hey!

The MEN *suddenly realise what they've done. They whoop, yell, embrace and slap each other while the* GIRLS *look on, smiling indulgently. The* MEN *stand grinning.*

SPACE 3: Sir! How about those omelettes, sir?
SPACE 4 & 5: Yummy!
SPACE 1 (*to* KITTY): Five hungry he-men here demanding their omelettes. Right, men?
MEN: Yes, sir!

The GIRLS *fall about laughing.*

SPACE 2: Come on! Where are they?
KITTY: I couldn't, er . . .
MOLLY: She couldn't catch the hens!
SPACE 3 (*unslinging his gun*): What's so funny?

Another rocket is heard, in the opposite direction from the first. ALL *stare towards it.*

SPACE 4: It's American, sir!

The tune of 'John Brown's Body' can be heard in the distance, coming nearer. The MEN *freeze as they listen and watch; the* GIRLS *look delighted.*

SPACE 1: Men!

MEN: Sir!

SPACE 1. A rocket from one of the American states has landed. Scatter!

The MEN grab their kit and run out the way they came, their guns at the ready.

GEORGINA: Men!

ALL: Men!

ALL turn with anticipation to see the newcomers. The music stops, then SPACE 6 races across the stage, his gun at the ready. He drops to the ground and beckons. One after another, the other members of MISSION TWO run on and kneel in an arc facing offstage and downstage, their backs to the pavilion. (They have already removed their helmets.) The GIRLS are nearly bursting with laughter, some stuffing handkerchiefs in their mouths to stop themselves laughing aloud.

SPACE 7: No sign of anyone, sir.

SPACE 6 (*standing*): I'm sure I saw something. All right, men, we can eat now. What's for lunch, Amos?

SPACE 8 (*unslinging his pack and looking inside*): Er, Davy Crockett's Old-Style Frontier Space Chow, sir. With blueberry pie and Space Coke.

MEN: Space Coke! Zowee!

As the MEN say this, the GIRLS mouth it with them, nodding their heads in chorus. KITTY, standing in the doorway, drops a tin tray as she laughs. The MEN whirl and drop, guns aimed.

KITTY (*picking up the tray*): Sorry!

The MEN straighten up, staring in bewilderment.

DOTTY: Welcome to Neptune!

Followed by the other GIRLS, DOTTY comes down, greeting and shaking hands with each man in turn. The other GIRLS do the same, then group themselves, smiling, opposite the MEN.

TERESA: Did you have a good journey?

SPACE 9: Er, we, er . . . Yes, we did!

MEN: That's right, we did!

GEORGINA: Isn't that nice?

GIRLS: Mmm.

AUGUSTA: From Earth, are you?

SPACE 8: From the independent American state of Mississippi.

EDWINA: And do you plan to stay long?

SPACE 6: We plan to settle here, lady!

GIRLS: Settle!

SPACE 9: Yup! Looks like good farming country!

SPACE 10: But mainly we aim to spread the Word.

MOLLY: What word is that?

SPACE 10: The Word of the Prophet Zachariah Chettle, miss!

SPACE 7: Zachariah Chettle had a vision in a dream!

SPACE 8: And in that vision he saw an angel!

SPACE 9: And that angel revealed the truth!

SPACE 10: And the truth is that all the words of the great prophets and teachers:

SPACE 6: Jesus.

SPACE 7: Mohammed.

SPACE 8: Buddha.

SPACE 9: Confucius.

SPACE 10: Are all one truth!

MEN: One truth! Halleluiah!

GIRLS: And what is the truth?

SPACE 9: That the Universe is ruled by love!

GIRLS: Love?

SPACE 6: Universal brotherly love.

GEORGINA: What about sisters?

SPACE 10: And he commanded his disciples to go forth through all the Universe to spread the word. So we came forth.

PEGGY: Eleventh.

POPPY: Twelfth.

MOLLY: Shut up, you two.

KITTY: Did you bring much food? We're rather low.

SPACE 8: Don't worry, little lady: we shan't be a burden on you.

SPACE 9: To eke out our rations, the ladies of our community had a monster baking day for us, and filled our good ship with thousands and thousands of fruit pies and meat pies!

SPACE 7: And thousands and thousands of bottles crammed with all manner of fruit and vegetables!

SPACE 10: That rocket is a veritable interplanetary horn of plenty: a cornucopia!

KITTY: Cornucopia! What an inspiring word!

SPACE 10: But not as inspiring, miss, as the Word of Zachariah Chettle. (*He produces a black book*) Accept this gift!

KITTY: Thank you. So this is the word of love?

SPACE 10: That's right, sister!

MEN: Halleluiah!

CISSIE: I'm sorry for being a stupid woman . . .

SPACE 9: Don't be sorry, sister: that's the way the Almighty made you.

CISSIE: Thank you. But if you come to spread love, why do you all carry guns?

AUGUSTA: I wondered that.

GIRLS: Me too.

SPACE 10: Because before the reign of love can begin, the Sons of Satan must be crushed and cast out!

MEN: Amen!

TERESA: And who are the Sons of Satan?

SPACE 7: The Sons of Satan are all those who do not accept the Word of Zachariah Chettle!

TERESA: I thought they might be.

AUGUSTA: If you try to crush anyone on Neptune, you'll be crushed yourself.

There is a muttered curse and a bang offstage. The MEN *whirl with guns at the ready.*

SPACE 6: What's that?

PEGGY: The atmosphere.

SPACE 6: Are you ladies alone on this planet?

GEORGINA: We've always been alone.
SPACE 6: That's good. Is that your flag?
GEORGINA: Er, yes, it is.
SPACE 6 (*to* SPACE 7): Take over!

SPACE 8 *removes the U.S.E. flag and gives it to* DOTTY.

SPACE 7 (*opening his pack*): What do you think I have here, ma'am?
GEORGINA: I can't imagine.
SPACE 7 (*producing it*): Look!
GIRLS (*with mock excitement*): It's a flag!

SPACE 7 *erects the flag while the* GIRLS *repeat the comments they made when the first flag was erected.*

SPACE 10: Quiet, please, ladies!

The MEN *line up and salute.* SPACE 10 *produces a transistor player which plays while the* MEN *sing. (Tune: 'John Brown's Body')*

MEN: Zachariah Chettle is the prophet of the Word;
    He is trampling out the vintage where the grapes of wrath are stirred;
    He shall elevate the Chosen and exterminate the herd:
      His truth is marching on!

CISSIE *starts to clap. The other* GIRLS *shush her.*

MEN: Glory, glory, halleluiah!
    Glory, glory, halleluiah!
    Glory, glory, halleluiah!
    His truth is marching on!

SPACE 10 *switches off the player.*

SPACE 6: And now for the marriage ceremony.
GIRLS: *The what?*
SPACE 8: Are any of you women already married?
GIRLS: No.

EDWINA: I don't want to be, either.

SPACE 10: It is unlawful for unmarried women to live alone.

GEORGINA: You mean, we have to marry you, now?

SPACE 6: It is according to the Word.

TERESA: But we haven't even been introduced!

KITTY: And there's ten of us and only five of you!

SPACE 7: The angel revealed to Zachariah Chettle that the Chosen may take as many wives as they can support. He himself had eighteen wives.

PEGGY: You mean, each of you is going to marry two of us?

SPACE 7: No.

PEGGY: Oh, good.

SPACE 6: The lower ranks will have one wife each. My Lieutenant will have three. As Leader I shall take four of you.

TERESA: I don't believe this!

SPACE 7: Are you opposing the Word of the Almighty?

TERESA: Well, no, but . . .

SPACE 7: Then let the ceremony proceed!

SPACE 10 *switches on the player, which plays suitable music. He then produces a large, imposing book and stands under the flag.*

SPACE 10: First, our Leader will choose his brides.

SPACE 6 *raises a finger to point out his brides when* SPACE 1 *appears with his gun pointed. He kicks over the player, which stops.*

SPACE 1: Hold it! Drop your guns!

The rest of MISSION ONE *appear alongside him with guns drawn.*

SPACE 8: Sons of Satan!

MISSION TWO (*raising their guns*): Sons of Satan!

DOTTY: Don't shoot! You'll kill yourselves!

MOLLY: We're warning you!

SPACE 1: In the name of the United States of Europe, I order you to drop your guns! Otherwise we shall be at war in (*Checking his watch*) one minute from now.

SPACE 6: The followers of Zachariah Chettle do not take orders from the Sons of Satan!

GIRLS: Here we go!

DOTTY: Take your seats, girls!

The two sides gradually back away from each other, spreading out, while the GIRLS go onto the verandah, where most of them sit. CISSIE sketches, MOLLY reads, another knits.

AUGUSTA: Don't say we didn't warn you!

SPACE 10 has retrieved the transistor player. He adjusts it and switches it on. It plays their hymn. SPACE 4 does likewise, and the Ode to Joy blares out. SPACE 1 looks at his watch and raises his hand. He drops it. SPACE 2 steps forward and takes aim.

GIRLS: Don't!

SPACE 2 fires, staggers and falls, dead. There is a short, very noisy battle, with bursts of (recorded) automatic fire and yells of encouragement and pain. Whenever a man shoots he dies with a yell, some staggering or falling into the wings or behind the pavilion. Some of the GIRLS watch, smiling sadly, others ignore it all. Finally SPACE 5 and SPACE 9 confront each other, shooting and falling simultaneously. The GIRLS look up. MOLLY slowly closes her book. PEGGY switches off MISSION TWO's transistor, while POPPY turns down the volume on the other, which continues to play the last minute of the Choral Symphony in the background.

GEORGINA: Guns and flags!

DOTTY: Put them with all the others.

The GIRLS come down and clear the stage. The guns and flags are put in the storeroom. When they open the door, it is seen to be crammed with flags and guns, some in racks on the inside of the door. The MEN are lugged out of sight. Some GIRLS take food from them and munch as they work. They look round, then go back onto the verandah and resume their knitting and reading, etc. The music ends.

CISSIE: What a beautiful day.

AUGUSTA: It's good to be alive.

GEORGINA: Yes.

DOTTY: This evening's poetry, Molly: anything fitting?

MOLLY (*looking through the book*): Here we are! By Christina
  Rossetti.

(*Reading*): I shall not see the shadows,
            I shall not feel the rain;
          I shall not hear the nightingale
            Sing on, as if in pain.
          And dreaming through the twilight
            That doth not rise nor set,
          Haply I may remember,
            And haply may forget.

As she reads, ALL *gradually become absolutely still. She closes the
book.*

POPPY: All that food.

ALL: Mmm.

DOTTY: Men!

TERESA: Funny creatures!

ALL: Mmm.

ALL *smile gently.*

(*Slow curtain*)

Castle Royal

CHARACTERS

MR SMITH (*later* KING)
MRS SMITH (*later* QUEEN)
PRINCE
PRINCESS
LANDLORD
BARMAID (DOLLY)
ALF (*Town Crier and Watchman*)
VAL (*Secretary and Messenger*)

Townsfolk

Uptowners	*Downtowners*
BEN	BOB (*later* GUARD 3)
DAN	JOE (*later* GUARD 4)
GUS	KEN
JIM (*later* GUARD 1)	ROY
TOM (*later* GUARD 2)	TED
LIZ	ANN
MEG	BEA
PAM	EVE
PAT	JEN
SUE	JOY

SCENE: The pub and town square of the capital of the smallest country in the world.

NOTE
For ease of reading, groups of characters are labelled ALL, MEN,

UPTOWNERS, etc. In rehearsal, the exact membership of each group can be defined more precisely.

It is hard to group characters on stage satisfactorily in scenes such as when the Prince and Princess are addressing the Townsfolk. One way is for all the Townsfolk to line up facing the audience with their backs to the Prince and Princess who stand on the platform behind them, also facing downstage.

The Play

*The set is used at first as the interior of the 'Pig and Whistle' pub and then
as the Town Square. Seats (preferably benches) and a bar, later used as a
platform. A litter-bin. A large inn-sign says 'Pig and Whistle'. A
signpost points to 'Uptown and Castle' and another to 'Downtown' and
'Out of Town'. When the play opens it is Friday night in the 'Pig and
Whistle'. The LANDLORD and BARMAID are behind the bar.
On one side sit the UPTOWNERS and on the other the
DOWNTOWNERS. ALL look glum. Nobody moves. Enter ALF,
who addresses the audience.*

ALF: Well, it's Friday night in the 'Pig and Whistle' in the capital
of the smallest country in the world. Market day. You'd expect
everybody to be happy. But are they happy?

ALL: No!

ALF: No, they are not. And why aren't they happy?

ALL: No money!

ALF: Hear that? No money. You see, every Friday the Uptown
farmers over there bring their veggies and eggs into town to sell
to the Downtowners. But they've sold hardly anything today,
'cause the Downtowners have . . .

DOWNTOWNERS: No money!

ALF: These Downtowners are tradespeople. They sell household
goods and so on to the Uptowners, but they've sold even less,
'cause the Uptowners likewise have . . .

UPTOWNERS: No money!

ALF: So, as you can see, they have a problem. Then someone had
an idea.

BOB: I got an idea!

ALL slowly look at BOB.

BEN: What's your idea, then?

BOB: My idea is, we get a King.

ALL: A King?

JEN: What do you want a King for? We haven't had a Royal Family for twenty years, have we?

ALL: No, we haven't.

JEN: And we don't want one.

EVE: Well, I do! I'm sick of cutting pictures of other countries' Royalty out of the papers. We should have our own, then we could hold our heads up high!

WOMEN: Hear, hear!

TED: And what about when they start pushing us around?

ROY: And who's going to pay for their robes and expensive meals and all their servants? We are!

PAT: Oh, come on! How many servants can they get in that little castle? It's only got two rooms!

ALL: Right!

BOB: Right, and Royalty nowadays don't actually push people around, do they? They just have their picture in the papers. And ours'll be in papers all over the world: King and Queen of the smallest country, living in the smallest castle.

JEN: So what's good about that?

BOB: What's good is tourists.

ALL: Tourists?

BOB: Yes! Tourists, holidaymakers. They'll stream in to look at our Royalty, they'll stay in our hotels and houses and they'll buy food from you and goods from us, and we can all buy from each other again, and we'll all be rich.

ALL: Rich! Cor!

BOB: Right. But first we need a Royal Family to bring in the tourists: agreed?

ALL: Agreed!

JOY: Well, how do you get a Royal Family?

KEN: Val can put an advert in the paper: 'Wanted, Royal Family'.

VAL: Right, I'll do that.

DAN: Hold on! I don't think these Royals read ordinary newspapers. I say Val writes a letter to all the Royals in the world, asking if they have a spare Prince and Princess who'd like to live in our castle and be our King and Queen.

VAL: Advert and letter, and give 'em a month to reply. Agreed?
ALL: Agreed!
VAL: Good: I'll start writing now.

> VAL *starts writing and* ALL *mime conversation.* ALF *rings his bell.* ALL *freeze.*

ALF: A month passed, and the day came round when all the replies were due in. Everybody in the 'Pig and Whistle' was excited.

> *He rings again and* ALL *mime excited conversation.* VAL *pulls out a briefcase and puts it on the bar.*

MEG: You got the replies from the Royals there, Val?
VAL (*patting the briefcase*): All here!
MEG: Read 'em out, then!
ALL: Yes!
VAL: Why not read 'em yourselves? Here you are!

> VAL *takes out as many envelopes as there are* TOWNSFOLK *and throws them around. Many are large and ornate, with crests.* ALL *scramble for them and exclaim.*

EVE: Ooh, look at this: 'From the Imperial Palace'!
JEN: 'From the castle of the Grand Duke!'
JOY: 'From the Celestial City!'
ALL: Aw!

> ALL *open an envelope, take out a letter and read.*

VAL: That's keeping 'em quiet.
LANDLORD: We're going to have a problem choosing from all that lot.
BARMAID: Be nice to have a King again. You reckon he'll drop in for a drink?
LANDLORD: No, these Royals are too superior to come into a pub. They'll just drive past in their carriage.

> *One after another* ALL *finish reading and sit blank faced.*

BEN: All finished?

ALL (*non-committal*): Yes.

BEN (*standing*): Right, who's going to kick off? (*To* KEN) What's yours say?

KEN (*reading*): 'Thank you for your request for a Royal Family. Unfortunately, all our Royals are spoken for. Good luck in your search. Yours sincerely, Grand Duke – ' Can't read it.

ALL: Aw!

VAL: Well, he's polite. (*To* TOM) Is yours?

TOM: He's not! He's just sent our letter back with 'You must be joking' scrawled across it.

ALL (*disgusted*): Cor!

PAT: Well, my Prince has sent a signed photo of himself.

ALL (*impressed*): Ooh!

PAT: But he doesn't want to come: castle's too small.

ALL: Aw!

ANN: And mine's not interested.

JEN: Nor mine.

JOY: Nor mine.

VAL: I don't believe this! They can't all turn their noses up at free accommodation and a gold crown. What about yours?

> VAL *asks each in turn, and* ALL *shake their heads and say 'No' until she comes to* JIM, *the last.*

VAL: I don't suppose yours is interested?

JIM: No, mine wants to come!

> ALL *cheer and scream with delight.*

VAL: Read it!

JIM: All right. (*Reading*) 'Yes! I would love to be your King! How do you punish criminals? I will bring my whip, also my guns. How soon can I start?'

ALL (*dismayed*): Guns! Cor!

JOE: What's he want to whip people for?

LIZ: He's weird: we don't want him.

ALL: No.

Silence. ALL *look at each other and the letters.*

VAL: Well, that's the lot.
JIM: And we're no nearer getting a Royal Family.
ALL: No.
JOE: And trade's going to get worse.
ALL: Right.

There is a loud knock at the door. ALL *look.*

LANDLORD: Come in!
ANN: Hey, perhaps it's a King and Queen!
ALL: Yes!
LANDLORD (*to* BARMAID): *Let 'em in!*

The BARMAID *lets in* MR & MRS SMITH. *They are an ordinary couple, possibly tall and wearing glasses and outdoor clothes. They stand smiling and blinking in the light.*

ANN: Tourists!
ALL: Just tourists!
MR SMITH: Not too late, are we?
LANDLORD: No, we don't close for another hour. What are you having?
MRS SMITH: Sorry, we don't drink.
LANDLORD: Ah, you want a room?
MR SMITH: No, we came about the castle.
LANDLORD: Oh, it's a bit late to look round there.
KEN: And it's pretty useless: I wouldn't waste time on it.
ALL: Nah!
GUS: I wouldn't keep pigs in that little castle!
ALL: Nah!
BARMAID: And you know it's empty?
MRS SMITH: Yes, that's why we came.
MR SMITH: About the advert.
VAL: You mean, for a King and Queen?
SMITHS (*smiling*): That's right!
MR SMITH: We've filled in an application form. Here.

VAL (*taking it*): You a King and Queen, are you?

SMITHS: Er, no.

PAM: Prince and Princess, are you, in disguise?

SMITHS (*smiling, embarrassed*): No, not actually.

DAN: Well, why have you applied, then?

ALL: Yeah!

MRS SMITH: Well, we've just got married, and we're seeking somewhere small to live, with a big garden, like your castle.

MR SMITH: We thought we might grow our own food, and be King and Queen in our spare time.

ALL (*disgusted*): Spare time!

VAL: I can't read your last name.

SMITHS: Smith.

ALL (*scornful*): Smith!

LIZ: We've had masses of letters from proper Royalty, haven't we?

ALL (*holding up letters*): Here!

MR SMITH: Oh, sorry to have bothered you. Come along, Helen.

MRS SMITH (*smiling*): Good night! Sorry!

The SMITHS *leave.*

LIZ (*scornful*): 'Sorry!' Huh! We want superior people, not Smiths.

JEN: But your superior people don't want to know, do they? I say these Smiths are our only chance. It's them or nobody.

BEA: Right! Let 'em be our Royalty, or we'll get no tourists and no money and this place'll be dead.

ALL: Right!

VAL (*to* BARMAID): Dolly, get your skates on and fetch 'em back. They can't have gone far.

BARMAID: Will do.

Exit BARMAID.

MEG: Here, how do we know they're going to rule us properly?

JEN: Like Bob said: Royals don't rule nowadays. This couple'll just dig their garden and have their pictures taken for the papers. Like figureheads, right?

ALL: Right!

VAL: All in favour of asking these Smiths to be our Royal Family?

ALL: All in favour!

Enter BARMAID, out of breath.

BARMAID: They're coming!

VAL: Right, ask 'em in.

BARMAID (*at door*): Would you come in, please?

The SMITHS enter and stand shyly in the doorway.

VAL: Come in, Mr and Mrs Smith. Are there any questions that you would like to ask us?

MR SMITH: I don't think so: it was all in the advert.

VAL: In that case, we would like to offer you the posts of King and Queen. Do you accept?

The SMITHS look at each other, smile and nod.

SMITHS: We do!

EVE: Long live our King and Queen!

ALL: Long live our King and Queen!

LANDLORD (*producing a box*): Right, here's the castle key, your Majesties. And a list of do's and don'ts: Keep your garden tidy, no coal in the bath and no pets. Oh, and you'll need these.

He pulls out two crowns, blows the dust off and casually polishes them. The SMITHS shyly put them on. Applause.

LANDLORD: Ladies and gentlemen, pray be upstanding! I give you a toast: The Royal pair!

ALL: The Royal pair!

KEN: Speech!

ALL: Speech!

MR SMITH: Well, my wife and I would like to thank you for choosing us, and we hope we shan't be too much bother.

MRS SMITH: And now, if you don't mind, we'd like to look round our new home and perhaps get some curtains up.

VAL: I'll show you the way.

MR SMITH: That's very kind of you. Good night!

ALL: Good night, your Majesties!

The SMITHS *and* VAL *go out.*

BEN: First thing in the morning we'll have 'em photographed. We'll issue new stamps and coins with their pictures on. And we'll announce the Coronation: that'll bring the tourists in!

ALL: Yes!

DAN: Coronation souvenirs! Mugs, plates with the Royal couple, teatowels! Tins of sweets and biscuits! T-shirts, flags, ashtrays, games, the lot! Anything with Royals on will sell! We've no time to waste: let's get working!

ALL hurry out chattering except LANDLORD *and* BARMAID. *The* LANDLORD *takes the sign down and starts work on the back of it. The sound of churchbells.*

ALL (*off*): Long live the King! Long live the Queen! Hurray!

LANDLORD: Look at that! A sign of better times!

He puts up the new sign: 'The Royal Arms'.

BARMAID: Ooh, lovely! Let's go see the procession!

LANDLORD *and* BARMAID *go out.* ALF *crosses, ringing his bell.*

ALF: One year later in the Town Square and all's well! One year later and all's well!

Enter LIZ, MEG, PAM, PAT *and* SUE. *Exit* ALF. (*As their talk becomes more heated, the* TOWNSFOLK *drift in and join in.*)

PAT: It's all very well him shouting 'All's well' but is it?

MEG: Well, it's not raining.

PAT: I'm talking about this so-called Royal couple.

ALL: Ah!

MEG: Well, look at all the tourists they've brought in.

PAT: Never mind tourists: I'm saying they're just not Royal enough.

A cycle bell is heard. The KING *and* QUEEN *wearing their crowns pedal a tandem across the stage in the direction of the castle. The* KING *rings the bell and they smile benignly.*

PAT: Whoever heard of a King and Queen riding a bicycle! And a tandem at that!

ALL: Right!

PAM: And they eat things they've grown themselves! Proper Royals eat banquets!

LIZ: And those clothes! Where did they buy them?

ALL: Oxfam!

PAM: And they never order us about! They don't have an air of Royalty!

ALL: No, they don't!

TOM: You're right. One night last week some youngsters were shouting in the square here, and Alf said he feared for his life. Then the Smiths turned up. And Alf thought 'Oh, good: they'll order them to be silent'.

ALL: And did they?

TOM: Did they heck! They wouldn't know how! No, they just stood there smiling.

ALL: Then what?

TOM: Well, the youngsters just quietened down and wandered off. No thanks to the Smiths.

JIM: I say, we've got the tourists coming in now, and we don't need these Smiths!

ALL: Hear, hear!

GUS: And I say, out with 'em, now!

ALL: Hear, hear!

ALF (*off*): Three wrecks in navy! Three wrecks in navy!

GUS: March to the castle!

ALF (*off, nearer*): Green flecks in gravy!

ALL: March to the castle!

ALL turn towards the castle. Enter ALF with a handbell. He takes a large sweet from his mouth, looks at it, then calls loud and clear:

ALF: Queen expecting baby! Queen expecting baby!

He walks off ringing his bell and chanting.

ALL (*sentimental*): Aw!
GUS (*starting to march*): To the castle!
ALL (*same tone as before*): Shut up!
GUS: To the . . .
ALL: Shut up!
JOY: A baby!
ALL: Aw! A Royal baby!
MEN: A little Prince!
WOMEN: A little Princess!
ALL: Aw!
BEA: I'm off to buy some pink wool to knit a little jacket for her.
KEN: I need some wood to make a little sword for him.

BEA *and* KEN *go out.*

SUE: I saw a lovely pattern!
ANN: Come on, before they sell out!

The WOMEN *hurry out.*

BOB: Off to the D.I.Y., men!

The MEN *trot off chanting 'D.I.Y.! D.I.Y.!'*

ALF (*off*): Nine months later and all's well!

ALF *enters.*

ALF: Nine months later and all's well!

Enter ALF *chanting. Enter the* WOMEN *carrying baby clothes. They look up at the castle.*

JEN: They say the doctors are up at the castle now.
JOY: And the midwife.

Enter the MEN *with toys.*

BOB: Any news?
WOMEN: Not yet.
ROY: I bet you twenty pounds it'll be a little Prince.
JEN: And I bet you twenty it'll be a little Princess.

    ALL *start saying 'Prince' or 'Princess'.*

BEN: Look! The flag's going up! Listen for the signal: one for a
    girl, two for a boy!
ALL: Shh!

    A cannon (or bell) is heard.

JEN: One! A Princess!

    ALL *with gifts for a Princess cheer.*

JEN: You owe me twenty pounds!

    The cannon sounds again. ALL *with boys' gifts cheer.*

ROY: Ha! Two for a boy! You owe me twenty!

    JEN *reaches into her purse, then a third cannon sounds.* ALL *look
up at the castle.*

ALL: Three. *Three*??
KEN: If it's one for a Princess and two for a Prince, what's three
    for?
EVE: I don't like to think.
ANN: Perhaps something's wrong!
TED: Here comes Val!

    VAL *runs in and stands panting.*

BEN: Anything wrong, Val?

    VAL *shakes her head.*

ANN: Has she had the baby?

    VAL *nods.*

BEA: Is she all right?

VAL *nods.*

MEG: We heard three. Is it a boy?
DAN: Or is it a girl?
JOE: Come on, put us out of our misery: is it a boy or a girl?
VAL (*recovering and looking round*): Yes.
ALL (*annoyed*): Aw!
BEA: Yes what? Boy or girl?
ALL: Is it a boy or is it a girl? Is it a girl or is it a boy?
VAL: It's both. It's twins. A boy *and* a girl.
ROY: I said a boy and I was right!
JEN: And I said a girl and I was right!
PAM: We were all right!
ALL: Hurray!
JOY: Sooner or later the King and Queen are going to get
    knocked off their tandem by a juggernaut and crushed, so which
    of the youngsters will be our ruler then?
ALL: That's right!
VAL: Who cares? I'm off to spread the news. 'Bye!
ALL: 'Bye!

ALL *line up and chant:*

MEN: Oh, we got a Prince!
WOMEN: Oh, we got a Princess!
MEN: We got a little boy
WOMEN: And we got a little girl.
MEN: And we know the little boy
        Is his Daddy's pride and joy
WOMEN: And the little girl is Mummy's pearl!

Two BABIES *cry off-stage.*

WOMEN: Hear those tiny angels call:
        We must take their presents.
MEN: Life round here for one and all
        Will be extremely pleasant!

WOMEN: 'Cause when our present King and Queen
         Get knocked from off their tandem
MEN: We shan't have to advertise
         For any old King at random.
WOMEN: 'Cause we have a little Princess
MEN: And we have a little Prince.
WOMEN: And that's a double guarantee
         That's certain to convince
ALL: That now we have a dynasty
         Of rulers who will give
         Us wealth and health and happiness
         As long as we shall live! Hurray!
SUE: Let's go sing to our little angels!

ALL cheer, turn, and dance off singing the song again. It fades. ALF's bell sounds. He enters carrying newspapers.

ALF: Prince and Princess start to walk! Read all about it!

He exits, rings his bell and re-enters.

ALF: Prince and Princess start school: exclusive pictures!

He exits, rings his bell and re-enters.

ALF: Prince and Princess growing up! Special Happy Family Supplement! Happy Royal Family!

Enter EVE with a Royal Family shopping bag.

ALF: Only a few left, lady.
EVE: Three, please. My kiddies love to cut out the pictures. Aren't we lucky, having such a happy Royal Family?

ALF exits shouting 'Happy Royal Family!' EVE reads. Enter ANN.

ANN: What are you reading?
EVE: Happy Royal Family.
ANN: You don't believe all that rubbish, do you?
EVE: They're a happy couple! You can see!

ANN: And what about those youngsters? Bad-tempered brats!

EVE: They're not! It says here 'The Prince and Princess enjoy a merry romp in the castle grounds'. Look!

ANN: My brother took those pictures, and he's never heard such language! She kept saying 'You can't make me: I'll do as I want', and her brother's saying 'Don't forget I'm a Prince'. They only kept still because he bribed 'em to.

EVE: I don't believe it.

ANN: Please yourself. I must rush: I've a houseful of tourists to feed. 'Bye!

    ANN *hurries out.* EVE *reads.*

ALF (*off*): Royal birthday! Special Supplement!

    ALF *enters with more papers.*

ALF: Royal twins eighteen today! Get your Special Birthday Supplement! Eighteen today!

EVE: Two, please.

ALF: Here you are, lady: add to your collection.

    ALF *exits shouting 'Royal Birthday! Special Supplement!' Enter* BEA *and* JOY.

BEA ⎫
JOY ⎭ : You don't believe all that rubbish, do you?

EVE: It says here: 'Our Prince and Princess like nothing better than a quiet evening with Mumsy and Dadsy, as they fondly call the Royal parents'.

BEA ⎫
JOY ⎭ : Quiet evening! Huh!

JOY: *She* spends her time at the pub!

EVE: Never!

BEA ⎫
JOY ⎭ : Always!

JOY: I was in there last night. She was giving the landlord lip when he called last orders, then her and her mates kept us awake till all hours, singing and shouting and banging on doors. When

Alf tried to stop 'em, she says 'You remember who I am!
There'll be big changes when I'm Queen!'

EVE: *He* doesn't go to the pub, the Prince.

BEA: Might be better if he did. He doesn't know how to enjoy
himself. He sneaks round with a little notebook.

EVE: Whatever for?

BEA: To snoop and spy and catch folk out for breaking rules.

JOY: Friend of mine opened her shop two minutes late, and there
he is on the doorstep saying 'Late again! If this happens when
I'm King I shall have to punish you!'

EVE: I wonder which will take over when the King and Queen
die?

BEA: I hope it's the Princess: at least we'll have fun.

JOY: I hope it's the Prince, for peace and quiet.

EVE: Perhaps they'll change. The King and Queen have years yet,
unless they get knocked off their tandem by a juggernaut.

    ALF's bell rings. Enter ALF.

ALF: Shock news from castle! Hear all about it! Shock news from
castle!

    The TOWNSFOLK *hurry in, chattering.*

MEG: They say they've been knocked off their tandem and
crushed!

ALL: Knocked off and crushed!

    A cycle bell rings. ALL *look.*

EVE: They're safe! They're here!

    Enter KING *and* QUEEN *(without crowns) on their tandem.*

ALL: Safe! Hurray!

ALF: Quiet, please, for the announcement!

ALL: Shh!

    The KING *and* QUEEN *climb up onto the platform.*

KING: Ladies and gentlemen, my wife and I have ruled now for, er . . .

QUEEN: Nineteen years.

KING: Nineteen years.

QUEEN: And in all that time we've never had a holiday. Nineteen years of digging and housework and bringing up children.

KING: So we've decided to take a break and pedal round the world before we're too old.

QUEEN: As you know, our son and daughter are eighteen now, old enough to rule. (*Gesturing*) Applause, please.

ALL *applaud politely and mutter as the* PRINCE *enters, neatly dressed, wearing glasses and carring a notebook, followed by the* PRINCESS *wearing jeans, hands in pockets. The* PRINCE *times the applause and makes a note, the* PRINCESS *chews.*

KING: We've given Val here a letter, to be opened only when we're out of sight, and it gives all the instructions you'll need. Goodbye to all of you!

The KING *and* QUEEN *mount their tandem and ride off calling "Bye!" ALL except the* PRINCE *and* PRINCESS *call after them "Bye! Ride carefully! Send us a postcard!" The bike bell sounds and* ALL *laugh.*

PRINCESS (*to* VAL): Give me that letter!

VAL: They're not out of sight yet! Your Dad said . . .

PRINCESS (*grabbing it*): Give!

PRINCE: I say . . .

PRINCESS: Shut your stupid trap, Fishface!

She rips open the letter and reads it.

PRINCE: It's addressed to both of us!

PRINCESS: Ladies first!

PRINCE: Here!

He gets hold of the letter and they read it together.

PRINCESS (*to* ALF): Give me a coin.
ALF: Here, your Highness.
PRINCESS (*to the* PRINCE, *spinning the coin*): Call!
PRINCE: Heads!
PRINCESS: Best of three! Call again!
PRINCE: I won!
PRINCESS: Call!
PRINCE: Heads!

> *She spins it again but drops it.*

PRINCE: That's heads again!
PRINCESS: No way! It doesn't count!

> *She runs off. He follows her.*

PRINCE: Give me that coin! I order you!
PRINCESS: You couldn't order a glass of water!
ALF: Can I have my pound back?

> *But they are off-stage.* ALL *stand depressed.*

SUE: They've dropped the letter: I'll go after them.
KEN: Why did they want a coin? Read it!
SUE: Ooh, no: it's not addressed to us!
KEN: But it's to do with us, and we ought to know who's in charge. Read it!
SUE: All right. (*Reading*) 'Dear Children, We are sick and tired of your constant quarrelling and selfishness . . .'
ALL: Oh!
SUE: 'So we have decided to leave the country for a spell. Ruling is easy if you use common sense. Take it in turns: a day each. Spin a coin for first go, and change when the Town Hall siren sounds. Your Loving Parents.'

> *A siren sounds.* ALL *look in that direction.*

ROY: One of 'em's in charge now. I wonder which?
JEN: One Royal's the same as another, I reckon. It's all a con to keep the workers down.

(Singing) Don't give them your loyalty,
        You who dig and delve.
        When you look up to Royalty
        You look down on yourselves.

    As she sings, the PRINCE *enters and writes in his book. The* OTHERS *try to warn her, but she doesn't notice.*

PRINCE: You!

JEN: Oh! Me, your Highness?

PRINCE: Yes, you! Why are you breaking Law 76 forbidding singing in the streets?

JEN: I've never heard of such a . . .

PRINCE: Ignorance is no excuse! Fined £10! Pay within a week or go to jail! Do not pass Go! Do not collect £200!

    ALL *laugh.* ROY *drops a crisp-packet.*

PRINCE: Stop laughing! *(Pointing)* What's that?

ROY: Crisp-packet. Salt and vinegar.

PRINCE: Crisp-packet, *your Highness*!

ROY: Crisp-packet, your Highness. Sorry I can't offer you one, but . . .

PRINCE: Litter! It's litter!

ROY: Oh, right, your Highness: it's litter.

PRINCE: Well, pick it up! This is a street, not a dustbin! Carry on working! *(Pointing)* Uptowners! Downtowners!

    He marches briskly out. UPTOWNERS *and* DOWNTOWNERS *split and begin drifting off to their homes.*

JEN: Ten pounds! Who's he think he is?

JOE: He thinks he's the master, and he is for today.

SUE: Well, I say he's right to clamp down on litter.

PAT: And on singing in the street.

UPTOWNERS: Hear, hear!

    By now the two groups are facing each other.

JOY: What's wrong with singing? It cheers you up!

DOWNTOWNERS: Hear, hear!
ANN: You lot wait till his sister takes over!
DOWNTOWNERS: Yeah! Just you wait!

Both sides start shouting insults at each other till ALF's bell is heard. They freeze. ALF *crosses the stage.*

ALF: Nine o'clock on a fine night and all's well! Nine o'clock on a fine morning and all's well!

Exit ALF. *The siren sounds. Enter the* PRINCESS *and* VAL *carrying a boxful of carnival masks.* ALL *relax.*

PRINCESS: Good morning, everybody!
ALL: Good morning, Princess!
PRINCESS: No boring laws today!
DOWNTOWNERS: Hurray!
PRINCESS: Because today I'm in charge and we're going to have fun! What are we going to have?
ALL: Fun!
PRINCESS: Right! Today is carnival day, so we're going to wear carnival masks!
TOM: You as well?
PRINCESS: 'Course I am! I'm just one of the girls! Get 'em on!

Music plays and VAL *gives out masks.* ALL *put one on except the* PRINCESS, ROY, LIZ, MEG *and* PAM.

PRINCESS (*to* ROY): Get your mask on!
ROY (*still with crisp-packet in his hand*): It's awkward with . . .
PRINCESS (*snatching it and dropping it*): Drop it! That's what litter's for! Brightens the place up!

She overturns the litter-bin and kicks the litter around. ALL *laugh except* LIZ, PAM *and* MEG. *She crosses to them.*

PRINCESS: Why are you three looking so sour?
LIZ: Because we see no reason to look happy.
PRINCESS: Don't come that with me! All wear a happy mask!
ALL: Get 'em on!

PRINCESS: You hear what they say? Get 'em on!

She puts on a mask and the three follow suit. ALL *cheer.*

PRINCESS: Are we all happy?
ALL: Yes, we are!
PRINCESS: What are we?
ALL: Happy!
PRINCESS (*singing*): I'm H-A-P-P-Y!

ALL join in the singing, and led by the PRINCESS *they form a line and dance off. Enter* ALF *with a big brush. He addresses the audience as he sweeps up.*

ALF: Well, it went on like this for a month or more. Days when the Prince was in charge, most folk went about quietly and minded their p's and q's. But every other day they went wild, laughing and singing. Some folk liked this day-on, day-off lark: they said it added variety to life. But a few Uptowners said the Prince didn't go far enough, because there was still some litter and stealing and that, 'cause I can't watch everybody, so they went to the Prince and he appointed new guards, and these guards . . .

Enter GUARDS *wearing uniform jackets and boots. They have truncheons and carry a black box which contains the crowns and enough plain masks for the other* TOWNSFOLK. *They also bring on a loudspeaker. They mime erecting a fence round one section of the stage.*

GUARD 1: Hey, you! You talking?
ALF: Yes, that's right.
GUARD 2: Not shouting, are you?
ALF: No, just talking quietly.
GUARD 3: You'd better be, 'cause it's jail today if you raise your voice. New open prison here.
GUARD 4: And it'll be jail tomorrow if you don't raise your voice, right?
ALF: Right.
GUARDS: So just watch out!

GUARD 1 (*to someone off-stage*): You there: shut your trap!

The GUARDS run off, keeping time.

ALF: Now, these guards were everywhere, every day. Prince's days, you had to be quiet; Princess's days, you had to look happy, or else! 'Course, the Prince and Princess could do as they liked. They seemed to get on a lot better nowadays. Certainly they both got a big kick out of putting people in jail.

Exit ALF. Enter PRINCE and PRINCESS in uniform jackets.

GUARD 1 (*off*): You! Pick that litter up! Come here!

GUARDS 1 & 2 run on with TED between them holding litter. They salute the PRINCE.

GUARD 2: Litter lout, your Highness!
PRINCE: One week in jail!

GUARDS 1 & 2 salute and run round the stage with TED, shouting 'Hup! Hup! Hup!'. They put a mask on TED, mime unlocking and opening a gate and push him in. TED mimes the size of the jail fence, putting his hands up to it, then he stands facing forward. The siren sounds. GUARDS 3 & 4 run in from the other side with PAT between them.

GUARD 3 (*saluting*): Grumbling in public, your Highness!
PRINCESS: Two weeks!
PAT: I really must complain . . .
PRINCESS: Three weeks!
PAT: Three!
GUARDS 3 & 4: Shut up!

GUARDS 3 & 4 march PAT to the jail shouting 'Hup! Hup! Hup!'. They put a mask on her and lock her in. She stands next to TED. The PRINCE and PRINCESS smile at each other and the GUARDS line up. ALF's bell rings and the TOWNSFOLK enter, glancing at the two prisoners and nudging each other.

PRINCE: Line up neatly and quietly. Quietly, I said!

The TOWNSFOLK *shuffle into place, helped by the* GUARDS, *who use their truncheons to prod them into neat lines.*

PRINCE: Faster next time! First, I call upon my sister to open our brand-new open-air prison!

PRINCESS: It gives me great pleasure to declare this splendid prison open to the public. May God bless it and all who serve in it!

ALL *clap, led by the* GUARDS.

PRINCE: Well said! Now, some of you are wondering about our parents.

ALL: Yes!

PRINCE: Well, we haven't heard from them for six months, and they are therefore officially listed as 'Missing, believed killed'. We are taking over for good.

TOWNSFOLK: Oh, no!

PRINCESS ⎫
PRINCE ⎭ : Oh, yes! Crowns!

GUARD 1 *runs to the box, takes out the crowns and gives them to the Royal pair.*

PRINCE (*crowning the* PRINCESS): Long live the Queen!

GUARDS: Long live the Queen!

ALL (*dutifully*): Long live the Queen!

The PRINCESS *crowns the* PRINCE.

ALL (*dutifully*): Long live the King!

PRINCE: Some of you have been complaining about our ruling a day at a time. You say you find it awkward for you.

TOWNSFOLK: That's right!

PRINCESS: Well, from now on we *shan't* be ruling a day each.

TOWNSFOLK: Oh, good!

PRINCESS: No, we'll be ruling for much shorter periods now.

TOWNSFOLK: Shorter??

PRINCESS: Yes, shorter. Are you all deaf?

PRINCE: We hope not, or you won't hear the whistle.

GUARD 1 *holds up a whistle and blows it.*

PRINCESS: When you hear that whistle . . .

PRINCE: It means that the rule has changed from the Queen to me.

PRINCESS ⎱
PRINCE ⎰ : Or vice-versa.

PRINCE: And it will blow whenever we like.

PRINCESS: One of us may rule for an hour.

PRINCE: Or two.

PRINCESS: Or five minutes.

PRINCE: Or one.

PRINCESS: Or just five seconds.

PRINCE: So this will really keep you all on your toes!

PRINCESS: And it will be much more fun!

PRINCE: But all you have to do to keep out of jail is to obey the rules!

PRINCESS: And remember, when I'm in charge the Number One rule is 'Look Happy'. What is it?

ALL: Look Happy!

PRINCE: But when I take over, what's the rule?

ALL: Peace and quiet!

PRINCE: Jolly good! And if you *are* good, you won't go to jail, will you?

ALL: No, your Majesty.

PRINCESS: So let's practise! Pretend I'm in charge, so the rule is . . .

TOWNSFOLK: Look happy.

PRINCESS: Well, look happy, then! Again!

TOWNSFOLK (*smiling desperately*): Look happy!

PRINCE: But when the whistle blows, the rule is . . .

TOWNSFOLK (*sad-faced but loud*): Peace and quiet!

PRINCE: Shh! Again!

TOWNSFOLK: (*quietly*): Peace and quiet.

PRINCE: Easy, isn't it?

TOWNSFOLK: Yes, your Majesty.

PRINCESS: And to make it even more fun, we're going to have background music. So let's start the practice with me in charge again! Ready? Look happy! Music! Go!

> GUARD 1 *switches music on and the* TOWNSFOLK *start miming everyday life: working and singing, walking and whistling or chatting loudly while the* GUARDS *patrol. Suddenly* GUARD 1 *blows, and* ALL *stop smiling and freeze except* GUS, *who has his back to* GUARD 1 *and continues smiling and singing loudly as he works.* GUARD 2 *grins, stalks up and hits him with his truncheon, accompanied by a loud noise. The* ROYALS *and* GUARDS *howl with laughter. Suddenly* GUARD 1 *blows again, and* ALL *begin to move, sing, etc. The* ROYALS *clap.*

PRINCE: Enough practising! All play for real this time!

PRINCESS: Me first again! Singalong time! Smile! The song is 'We love to labour laughingly' and the tune is 'Tannenbaum'. And you'd better like it: it's jail if you don't!

> *The* GUARDS *and* ROYALS *laugh, followed by the* TOWNSFOLK.

PRINCESS: All ready? Go!

> *The* TOWNSFOLK *grin,* GUARD 3 *switches on the music and all the* TOWNSFOLK *work, etc, and sing:*

TOWNSFOLK (*singing*): We love to labour laughingly
>> For our Prince and Princess.
>> We march around so merrily
>> For our Prince and Princess . . .

> *As they sing, they keep a wary eye on* GUARD 1. *Suddenly he blows.* GUS *and* SUE *are caught out.* GUARDS *rush and hit them. They yell, but are hustled into jail and masked as the* ROYALS *hoot with laughter. They stand next to* TED *and* PAT.

PRINCE: Hard luck, you two! And two weeks' hard labour! Off we go! Peace and quiet!

GUARD 1 *blows. Music plays quietly and* ALL *move busily but silently.* GUARD 1 *blows sooner than before, and three people are taken by surprise.* GUARDS *rush them to jail where they don masks and join the others. The game continues, alternately noisy and quiet, with* GUARD 1 *sometimes starting the game only to stop it instantly. The* ROYALS *clap and cheer. Now only* JEN *is left. For several changes she keeps out of jail, but when she takes her eyes off* GUARD 1, *he throws the whistle to* GUARD 2 *and puts his hands in his pockets.* JEN *starts singing, and* GUARD 2 *blows, just audibly. She continues singing for a second.*

PRINCESS ⎫ . Out! Go straight to jail! Do not pass Go!
PRINCE   ⎭ : Do not collect £200!
JEN: No! It's a cheat!

But the GUARDS *take* JEN, *shouting and struggling, into jail and mask her while the* PRISONERS *protest. The* GUARDS *lock the 'gate' and line up facing the* PRISONERS, *whose hands define the 'fence'.*

PRINCESS ⎫
PRINCE   ⎭ : Silence! Quiet! Shut up!

But the PRISONERS *still protest. The* GUARDS *produce guns. The* PRISONERS *moan.*

PRINCESS: Stop that dreary moaning! This is your last chance!

The PRISONERS *continue to complain.*

PRINCE: Guards! One step forward! Take aim!

The GUARDS *step forward and raise their guns. Unseen by them or by the* PRINCE *and* PRINCESS, *the* KING *and* QUEEN *enter with their tandem. The* PRISONERS *see them and say 'Aw!'. The cycle bell rings. Hesitantly, the* GUARDS *lower their guns. The* QUEEN *switches off the music and the* KING *parks the bike. They go to their children and each holds out a hand. Wordlessly the* PRINCE *and* PRINCESS *remove their crowns and hand them over.*

QUEEN: Thank you, children.

The QUEEN *and* KING *throw the crowns over the 'fence', to be caught by the* PRISONERS.

KING: Let's see your faces!

The PRISONERS *remove their masks.*

QUEEN: And let's see people without uniforms!

The GUARDS *look at each other, then remove their jackets.*

QUEEN: And you two: no uniforms!
PRINCESS ⎫
⎬ : But we . . .
PRINCE ⎭
KING: But nothing! They belong to your mother and me. We've never worn them because they look ridiculous.
QUEEN: And they make you behave ridiculously. Take them off! And let our people go!

GUARD 1 *unlocks the 'gate' and the* TOWNSFOLK *walk out, giggling at the* PRINCE *and* PRINCESS *as they remove their jackets. The* PRINCESS *wears an old T-shirt and the* PRINCE *a vest. They stand downstage, their backs to the others.*

KING: Do you think it's right to threaten people with guns?
PRINCESS ⎫
⎬ : Yes, we do.
PRINCE ⎭
KING: Oh, I see. Guards, raise your guns!

The GUARDS *raise their guns to point at the young pair.*

KING: And is it right to shoot those who don't do what you want?

The PRINCE *and* PRINCESS *stand silent.*

KING: I'm not sure you've learned your lesson. (*To the* GUARDS) I told you to raise your guns. Raise them!

The GUARDS *raise their guns till they point to the sky.*

QUEEN (*mouthing silently to the* TOWNSFOLK): One, two, three, fire!

KING: One, two, three . . .

ALL (*very loud, clapping or stamping*): Fire!!

The PRINCE *and* PRINCESS *yell with fright, then turn and laugh with relief.* ALL *join in.*

KING: Now have you learned your lesson?

PRINCESS ⎫
PRINCE ⎭ : Yes!

QUEEN: I think they have. (*To the* PRINCE) Learn to laugh at yourself, then no-one else will.

KING (*to the* PRINCESS): It's good to have fun, but don't stop other folk having theirs. Remember!

PRINCESS ⎫
PRINCE ⎭ : We'll remember.

KING: Yes, I think you will.

ALL applaud. A clock starts to strike.

DAN: Time for bed.

ALL (*starting to go*). Mmm.

TED: Wait! What law do we follow tomorrow?

QUEEN: There's only one law, and we all know it. It's the law of . . .

ALL: Common sense!

QUEEN ⎫
KING ⎭ : Can't hear you!

ALL (*loud*): Common sense!

QUEEN: And don't let any of us forget it, ever again.

GUARD 1: What about our guns?

QUEEN: In the bin!

ALL applaud as the GUARDS *drop their guns in the bin.*

BEN: And what about these crowns?

KING: Back in the box.

The crowns are put in the box. ALL *applaud.*

KING: Tomorrow we'll make a new start. Good night, everyone.
ALL: Good night!

The TOWNSFOLK *start to leave, saying their good nights.*

EVE: It's good to have you back, your Majesty.
QUEEN: It's good to *be* back. I like cycling, but you can have too
    much of anything.
BEA: We all found that out. (*To* PRINCE *and* PRINCESS) Didn't
    we? Good night.
ROYALS: Good night!

ALL *have gone except the* ROYALS.

QUEEN (*to* PRINCE *and* PRINCESS): Clean up here in the
    morning. Put things straight.
PRINCESS ⎫
PRINCE   ⎬ : Will do.
KING: You two take the box; we'll bring the bike.
PRINCESS ⎫
PRINCE   ⎬ : Right!

As they go, ALF *calls off-stage 'Ten o'clock on a fine night and all's well'. He enters carrying a bin-liner.*

ALF: Ten o'clock on a fine night and all's well!

He looks at the masks and jackets and shakes his head, then he empties the litter-bin into his liner. He takes up a gun, shakes his head again and drops the gun in. Then he slings the liner on his back and goes out calling 'Ten o'clock on a fine night and all's well!'.

(*Curtain*)

Soft Soap

CHARACTERS

Men	Women
SOAPY, *a salesman*	ANNI
OLAF, *the leader*	BRIGID
HARALD, *his lieutenant*	FREDA
BENNI	GUDRUN
BIORN	HELGA
ERIK	HILDA
FINN	INGRID
FRITH	ISLA
GAML	JENNI
IVAR	KARIN
MAGNUS	KATI
OTTO	LIV
SWAIN	MARGIT
ULRIC	OLGA

SCENE: A Viking settlement by a river in England, over 1,000 years ago.

The Play

Enter ANNI *and* MARGIT *carrying washing-baskets.* ANNI *looks round, puzzled, while* MARGIT *comes forward, puts down her basket, takes out a block of coarse soap and a shirt, and starts washing it in the river between actors and audience.*

ANNI: Hey, where are all the other women? It is wash-day today, isn't it?

MARGIT (*flinging the shirt down*): Oh, no!

ANNI: What's wrong?

MARGIT: How does he expect me to get his clothes clean in a freezing river? (*Holding up the shirt*) Look at this: all greasy!

ANNI: It's this soap: it's useless.

MARGIT: It's not just the soap, Anni, you know that!

> MARGIT *and* ANNI *start rubbing their washing hard. Enter* HARALD *leading the* OTHER WOMEN *who are carrying a small table, a chair and some stools or benches. They put them down and stretch.*

HARALD: You can't wash here today: move!

MARGIT: Why? It's washing-day.

HARALD: It's the men's meeting, isn't it?

MARGIT
ANNI } : Aw, no!

HARALD (*to the* OTHER WOMEN): Well, don't just stand there like fools! Set 'em out: now!

> *Exit* HARALD. *The* WOMEN *reluctantly set out the seats.* SOME *sit.*

KATI: Charming manners our men have.

ISLA: Yes. One day I'll meet a man who talks nicely to me.

HELGA: And when you do, don't trust him!

> *Laughter.*

FREDA: Why can't the men set their own seats out?

OLGA: 'Cause it's a woman's job.

FREDA: Why?

GUDRUN: Because just about everything's a woman's job, isn't it? Always has been, always will be.

JENNI: And why do they have to meet on a Thorsday? Don't they know it's washing-day?

BRIGID: They know, but they don't care! Men! I'd like to tell 'em what I think of 'em.

OLGA: Well, why don't you speak up at the meeting?

GUDRUN: Talk sense! Since when were women allowed to speak?

KARIN: If we were, we'd get something done. Men yack non-stop and get nowhere.

HELGA: Right, like why are they still meeting outside? We've been in England six months and they haven't even built a meeting-house yet!

HILDA: They said they couldn't find the timber.

HELGA: They found the timber for the ale-house fast enough! They're all down there now.

INGRID: Right. And what about our wash-house? They agreed to start on it last month, but they've forgotten all about it. Come Winter, our fingers'll be frozen to the bone, washing in this river.

A bell tolls off-stage.

GUDRUN: Meeting-bell.

BRIGID: What say we hang around and see what they decide?

JENNI: If they let us.

ISLA: Hey! There's a man watching us over there!

HELGA: Perhaps he's the one who's going to talk nicely!

ALL laugh, staring off-stage.

ANNI: It's a stranger. He's not a Viking like us.

LIV: 'Course he is! Don't you recognise him? Oh, what did they call him back home? Was it Dopy?

KATI: No, Soapy!

WOMEN: Soapy: that's right!

KATI: And the lads always mocked him. They called him Soft Soapy.

GUDRUN: Yes, I used to feel sorry for him.

WOMEN: Mmm.

KARIN: He was clever, but I never quite trusted him.

INGRID: Right! He tried to con me once with a dud coin.

FREDA: Perhaps he's changed.

HILDA: I wonder what he's doing over here?

OLGA: We'll find out: he's coming.

Enter SOAPY *carrying a big shoulder-bag.*

SOAPY: Good morning, ladies!

WOMEN: Hello, Soapy!

SOAPY: Oh, you recognise me!

OLGA: 'Course we do! Where've you been hiding yourself all these years?

SOAPY: Oh, I've just finished, er, college in Denmark.

WOMEN: College! Fancy that!

BRIGID: And what did you study at this college?

SOAPY: A new course: salesmanship and business studies.

BRIGID (*disbelieving*): Go on!

JENNI: So what's your business here?

SOAPY: I want to help housewives like yourselves.

FREDA: A man wanting to help women! Pull the other one!

Laughter.

BRIGID: Come clean: what do you want from us, Soapy?

SOAPY (*taking out a notebook*): Frankly, I'd like to ask you a few simple questions.

FREDA: And how does that help us?

WOMEN: Yes!

SOAPY: Well, suppose I told you that there are useful gifts for the best answers?

WOMEN: Ooh! Useful gifts!

INGRID: Go on, ask us. We've nothing better to do. Sit down, girls.

The WOMEN *sit.*

SOAPY: Thank you! Could I ask first if there's a place of worship here?

KATI: No, we haven't got a church built yet. We worship Thor at Olaf's house.

SOAPY (*writing*): So Olaf's head man. No church. And you don't have a priest?

WOMEN: No, no priest.

SOAPY (*writing*): No priest. And can I ask, if there was a church here, would you attend it?

ANNI: Well, I would. I love singing.

KARIN: Me too. I think most of us would.

WOMEN: Mmm.

LIV: I don't know about the men. Not hymns. They're more for drinking-songs in the pub.

HELGA: Can I put a question to you: why are you asking us this?

SOAPY: We're trying to identify housewives' social needs. Now, dare I ask how much your men give you for housekeeping?

Silence. The WOMEN *look at each other, embarrassed.*

OLGA: We'd rather not answer that.

ANNI: I'll tell him! We get no money at all! We have to swap things amongst ourselves.

HILDA: She's right: the men keep all the money to buy ale.

WOMEN: That's right.

SOAPY (*making notes*): I see. And a final question: what sort of soap powder do you use?

WOMEN (*amazed*): Soap powder? What's that?

SOAPY: It's a brand new product. Housewives who use it report that their clothes look cleaner, last longer and smell sweeter than clothes washed with old-fashioned soap in river water! And for the clever ladies who answered most questions, here are free packets of (*producing them*) Thoril!

SOAPY *gives out packets of Thoril to* HILDA, KARIN *and* ANNI *as the* OTHERS *applaud.*

SOAPY: Try this next time you do your wash. And remember the name: Thoril!

WOMEN (*inspecting the packets*): Ooh, Thoril!

HILDA: Thank you very much. Why not stay and meet the menfolk?

MARGIT: Yes, it's their monthly meeting today: see what you make of it.

ISLA: Move: they're coming now.

The WOMEN *and* SOAPY *move to one side.* FINN *and* FRITH *run in.*

FINN: Aw, we're early: nobody here but women.

FRITH (*seeing* SOAPY): Hey, I know that face! It's Soapy, the lad with an answer for everything!

FINN: What's he doing here?

SOAPY (*coming forward*): I'm selling stationery and household products. Can I interest you in . . . ?

FRITH: No, you can't. If you deal with women's things you'd best stay with 'em. Women and outsiders can't vote, you know.

FINN: The others are coming.

The OTHER MEN *can be heard singing. They enter with their arms round each other.* (OLAF *is more richly dressed than the rest.*) *They sing their song, with* FRITH *and* FINN *joining in.*

MEN: We landed next to a pub in Hull
    And the landlord said 'I'm sorry, we're full'.
    We said 'Just a minute, old pet!'
    Then we chased the others out and we drank their stout,
    'Cause what we want, we get!
      Oh, it's to my liking,
      Being a Viking,
      That's the life for me!

Then we sailed up the Humber
And met English without number
Who tried to make us stop.
But we made 'em fight for a day and a night –
Now we're the blokes on top!
    Oh, it's to my liking,
    Being a Viking,
    That's the life for me!

Then we drank more booze
And we sailed up the Ouse
Till we came to the city of York.
They said 'You have no right to be here',
So we chucked 'em in the river and we drank their beer
'Cause fighting's better than talk!
    Oh, it's to my liking,
    Being a Viking,
    That's the life for me! Hey!

OLAF (*spying* SOAPY): Who's that bloke? What's he doing here?

HILDA: An old friend of ours. He's just watching.

OLAF: Soapy! Making yourself at home with the women?

SOAPY: May Thor go with you, Olaf.

OLAF: And with you. Stay around: you might learn something.

ULRIC: How d'you get here, Soapy: swim?

OTTO: Nah, he never learned – too busy wasting his time reading and writing.

SOAPY: They say the pen is mightier than the sword.

OTTO: Not round here, mate!

    The MEN *laugh.*

OLAF: Cut the cackle and sit down!

    The MEN *sit, with* OLAF *taking the chair.*

HARALD: We're not letting the women stay, are we?

SWAIN: Yes!

OTTO: No!

Immediately the MEN *start squabbling loudly, shouting 'Yes!' or 'No!' and squaring up to each other while the* WOMEN *call comments.*

OLAF (*very loud*): Shut up!

Instant silence.

OLAF: Sit down or I'll knock you down!

ALL *settle down.*

OLAF: Right: pin your lugs back! I'm the boss here, and I say we'll have a proper monthly meeting for a change. No more shouting and fighting: understood?
MEN: Understood.
OLAF: Right, who wants to throw the first words in? Anybody can speak.
FREDA (*raising a hand*): I do. I'd just like to ask . . .
MEN: Shut up!
FREDA: You said anybody could speak.
OLAF: Anybody except women. Women aren't anybody.
MEN: Right!
OLAF: Right. Any man got anything to say?
IVAR (*raising a hand*): My wife says . . .
MEN (*mocking*): Ooh! 'My wife says!'
IVAR: My wife says what did we decide last time about building a wash-house, 'cause the bad weather's coming on.
OLAF: Right, that's the first thing. So, what did we decide?
SWAIN: Erm, we agreed that four of us . . .
ERIK: Three!
OTTO: Five!
SWAIN: Well, we agreed that some of us would make a start on the building last Moonsday
FRITH: No, Thorsday!
ULRIC: No, Wodensday!

ALL *start calling out different days.*

OLAF: Shut it! (*To* SWAIN): Carry on.

SWAIN: We definitely decided that some of us would start building.

OLAF: Well, has anybody started?

ALL (*looking at each other*): No.

OTTO: Anyway, it wasn't a wash-house we agreed on: it was a boat house.

SOME MEN: Right!

BIORN: Oh, I thought you said 'goat-house'. I voted for a goat-house, not a boat-house.

ALL (*annoyed*): Oh!

ERIK: Goats! What's wrong with sheep?

BIORN: Goats give better milk than sheep.

ERIK: Well, goats stink.

IVAR: Listen who's talking!

ERIK (*crossing to* IVAR): You saying I stink?

ALL: Sit down!

ERIK *resumes his seat.*

OLAF (*banging the table*): Stop talking out of order! So last time we definitely decided to start building something, somewhere, sometime?

MEN: Yeah, definitely.

INGRID: Men, the great thinkers! Huh!

WOMEN: Huh!

OLAF: Look, what do you women want here?

JENNI: We want somebody who can run a meeting properly!

BRIGID: And we want a wash-house, don't we, girls?

WOMEN: Yes!

BRIGID: What do we want?

WOMEN: A wash-house!

BRIGID: And when do we want it?

WOMEN: Now!

BRIGID (*chanting*): We want a wash-house!

The WOMEN *take up the chant of 'We want a wash-house!'
clapping rhythmically and building up to a climax. They fall
silent.*

HARALD: I vote that the women go and do their washing in the
river now.

OLAF: All agreed?

MEN: All agreed!

WOMEN: Aw, it's not fair!

BRIGID: What about building our wash-house?

ANNI: Leave 'em: they couldn't build a dog-kennel.

HILDA: Let's go and try this new powder!

KARIN: Great idea! Come on! Hey, look what it says on the
packet!

The WOMEN *go out chattering.*

HARALD: We'll get on better without them interrupting.

OLAF: We couldn't get on any worse, could we?

SOAPY *steps forward and raises a hand.* ALL *stare.*

SOAPY: May I make a suggestion, Olaf, sir?

OLAF: Eh?

SOAPY: To avoid unnecessary argument, why not keep minutes
of your meetings?

MEN: Minutes?

SOAPY: That's right. (*Producing a large book*) All you need is a
minute-book like this, and every time you decide something
you write it down. For example, you might write 'On
Wodensday the twelfth we agreed by nine votes to four to build
. . .' whatever you agreed on. It only takes a minute: that's why
it's called a minute-book. And once it's written, there's an end
to argument. As the poet says:

> 'What is written must be true:
> Letters never lie.
> Tongues are snakes that hiss and weave
> Cunning patterns to deceive.

> Writing's what we must believe,
> Thanks to Thor on high.'

Applause.

OLAF: Very nice. How much?

SOAPY: Just one silver piece.

OLAF: Right, we'll have one of them. (*To* HARALD) Pay him.

HARALD: Why me?

OLAF: Pay the man!

HARALD (*paying* SOAPY): Here!

SOAPY: Thank you, sir. You will also need (*producing the items as he speaks*) a pen, a pen-knife and a bottle of ink.

HARALD (*ironic*): Oh, is that all?

SOAPY: No, sir: you need a small box of special sand to stop your ink blotting. Just another four pieces of silver.

Laughter.

HARALD (*paying him*): You haven't changed, have you? Is *that* all?

SOAPY: That's all! Now you can write what you decide.

OLAF: Good! We shall now vote on what to build next. (*To* SOAPY) You count, then there's no cheating. Hands up for a wash-house!

Less than half the MEN *raise their hands.*

OLAF: Anyone for a goat-house?

BIORN (*raising both hands*): Me!

Laughter.

OLAF: Boat-house!

The REST *raise their hands.*

OLAF: Right! That's decided!

Those who have voted for the boat-house cheer.

GAML: Back to the pub!

MEN (*standing and starting to go*): Back to the pub!

BENNI: Wait a minute! Who's going to write it down?

The MEN *look at each other, embarrassed.*

MAGNUS: Swain can do joined-up writing.

SWAIN: Aw, not me! I can't spell long words!

OLAF: Anybody else? Come on! Somebody's got to write these, er . . . seconds.

SOAPY: Minutes.

OLAF: That's what I meant.

FINN (*indicating* SOAPY): What about him? He reckons to be brainy: why can't he write 'em?

BENNI: 'Cause he doesn't live here, does he?

IVAR: And he won't be here next time.

FINN: Why not? I say let him live here and be our clerk.

BIORN: What sort of job is that for a real man? I wouldn't do it, even if you paid me.

MEN: No!

FINN: Well, if none of us'll do it, somebody else has to, and we can't ask a woman, or she'd take over.

Laughter.

OLAF: Right! Who's in favour of asking Soapy to stay here and work for us as our clerk? I'm sure he'll find other things to write.

ALL *except* SWAIN *and* ULRIC *raise their hands.*

OLAF: Any against?

SWAIN *and* ULRIC *raise their hands. The* REST *jeer.*

OLAF: Right! We've voted for you to be our town clerk. You write what we tell you and the rest of your time's your own. What do you say? It's easier than being a travelling salesman.

SOAPY: Er . . . Can I have my own house?

The MEN *look at each other and nod.*

OLAF: Yes, we'll build you a cottage and you can have two good meals a day like everybody else.

SOAPY: I want three.

ALL: Three?

SOAPY: Yes, 'cause my brain-cells need more nourishment.

MEN (*looking at each other*): Nah!

OLAF: No, two's enough. Come on: your own little house and two good meals a day just for doing a bit of pen-pushing.

SOAPY *looks round and ponders, then decides.*

SOAPY: All right!

The MEN *applaud and* OLAF *shakes* SOAPY'*s hand.*

SOAPY: Thank you. I'll write up this meeting and I'll also write down all the laws of Thor in case of dispute.

SWAIN: How come you know all these laws? I thought you were a salesman?

SOAPY: Erm, yes, but I qualified as a priest of Thor as well. Here's my certificate if you'd like to see it. It's in Danish.

He holds up an elaborate certificate. ALL *nod, impressed.*

BENNI: That proves he's the man for the job.

OLAF: Right, Soapy: your first job is to get the minutes and the laws down in the book. Are you coming back to the pub with us? It's good ale.

SOAPY: Sorry, I must write your minutes. And actually I never touch alcohol: I prefer water.

MEN: Water! Yeucch!

OTTO: Well, there's enough water in the river!

Laughter.

OLAF: Give him his gear if he's staying!

HARALD *puts the writing equipment on the table.*

SOAPY: Thank you so much!

HARALD: You're welcome.

GAML: Last one in the pub buys the drinks!

MEN: Yeah!

Shouting, they run out. SOAPY *looks after them, smiling and rubbing his hands, then he sits down and writes.*

GUDRUN (*off*): Oh, no!

GUDRUN *hurries in with the* OTHER WOMEN.

LIV: Well, it must be true that he's the town clerk.

GUDRUN: Soapy! Is it true what my man says, that they've agreed to build a boat-house instead of a wash-house?

ISLA: It's disgusting!

KATI: If men had to do the washing it'd be different!

BRIGID: Are you writing down what they decided?

SOAPY: Yes. Listen! (*Reading*) 'Minutes of meeting held on Thorsday the thirteenth. It was decided that the priest should have his own house and three meals a day.'

WOMEN: Three?

SOAPY: That's what it says. (*Reading*) 'It was also decided by seven votes to five that the next public building should be . . .'

WOMEN (*gloomily*): Go on!

SOAPY: 'A wash-house.'

WOMEN: What??

SOAPY: A wash-house.

LIV: But my man's sure they voted for a boat-house.

WOMEN: That's right.

SOAPY: No, it says here in writing: 'Wash-house', and if it's written it must be true.

KATI: We're going to get a wash-house!

The WOMEN *cheer, scream and clap.*

SOAPY (*raising a hand*): And old-fashioned soap has no place in a modern wash-house, so let's see the three lucky ladies who won the free packets of Thoril!

He takes KARIN, HILDA *and* ANNI *on one side, and talks to them while the* OTHER WOMEN *improvise a dance, chanting 'We've got a wash-house!' They sit, laughing.*

OLGA: Hey, these seats are for men only!

FREDA: Oh, yes? Where's it say that?

BRIGID: Hey, write in the book: 'It was agreed that anybody can sit anywhere, anytime.'

WOMEN: Yes!

SOAPY: Ah, ah! I can only write the truth!

WOMEN: Aw!

SOAPY: But listen to these ladies who are going to tell us about something that can change our lives!

ALL *clap as* HILDA, KARIN *and* ANNI *hold up their Thoril packets, then step forward, each carrying two garments.*

HILDA (*holding up a stained garment*): My husband's shirt was always filthy. I could not get the stains out with old-fashioned soap and water, however hard I rubbed. But no stains now, thanks to Thoril! (*Holding up clean garment*)

Applause.

KARIN: My man likes killing things.

WOMEN: Ugh!

KARIN: And his clothes got covered in blood. (*Holding up bloody garment*) But thanks to Thoril, they are now whiter than white! (*Holding up clean garment*)

Loud applause.

ANNI: My husband's manners are disgusting.

INGRID: Aren't they all?

WOMEN: Yes!

ANNI (*holding up a shirt covered in multi-coloured stains*): Look at all these stains: egg, gravy, mustard, er . . .

SOAPY: Blackcurrant juice.

ANNI: Blackcurrant juice, tomato sauce and Irish stew.

WOMEN: Ugh!

ANNI: But now, thanks to miracle Thoril, all his clothes are dazzling white!

She holds up a dazzling garment. The WOMEN scream and clap.
SOAPY *produces another packet, then he and the THREE*
WOMEN, *swaying and holding their packets, sing:*

SOAPY, HILDA, KARIN, ANNI:
> If your shirt is covered in dirt,
> Use Thoril!
> If you've got a filthy jacket
> Then you need to get a packet
> Of Thoril!
> And if you've got a stubborn stain,
> No need to rub that stain in vain,
> No need to suffer or complain:
> Use Thoril!

Applause.

SOAPY: And would any of you go back to old-fashioned soap?
WOMEN: No!
SOAPY: I'm offering you ten blocks of old-fashioned soap for one
packet of Thoril!
WOMEN: No way!
SOAPY (*to the audience*): Yes, these ladies have found out for
themselves why Thoril is the only powder recommended by top
gods! (*To the* WOMEN) So all you need now is the money to
buy a packet!
WOMEN: Money!
KATI: We told you: we have no money.
GUDRUN: And no chance of getting any, have we?
WOMEN (*glumly*): No.
KATI (*raising a hand*): You asked about church services: I say let's
have one to pray for money.
SOAPY: Brilliant idea! We'll meet here this afternoon. Just now I
have to write out the laws and arrange the building of my
cottage and your wash-house. 'Bye!
WOMEN: 'Bye!

Exit SOAPY.

MARGIT: A wash-house! I can't believe it!

INGRID: My man isn't going to believe it either: he's dead certain they voted for a boat-house.

HELGA: Well, it's written down, so they can't change it!

WOMEN: No!

HELGA: Thanks to Soapy!

WOMEN: Yes!

KARIN: He's a man who understands women.

JENNI: I still don't trust him.

BRIGID: Me neither.

OTHERS: Aw, why not?

BRIGID: He doesn't look you in the eye.

JENNI: And I don't believe all that talk about college.

MARGIT: Well, I wish my man talked like he does.

ANNI: I think he talks lovely.

WOMEN: Hear, hear!

HILDA: And he doesn't swill beer like all our men, either!

GUDRUN: He's bringing good luck to all of us!

OLGA: And our bad luck is we have housework to do. Come on!

ALL *except* JENNI *and* BRIGID *go out talking.*

BRIGID: So why is this guy so keen to get a wash-house built, Jenni?

JENNI: It's part of some scheme to rip us off.

BRIGID: Yes. What say you and me keep an eye on him?

JENNI: Good thinking. Let's go!

JENNI *and* BRIGID *go out. Enter* OLAF, HARALD *carrying plans and* SOAPY *with the minute-book.*

OLAF: What did we decide to build first?

HARALD } : The boat-house.
SOAPY }   The manse.

OLAF }   : The what?
HARALD }

SOAPY: The manse, where the priest lives. You all agreed I could have my own place, didn't you?

OLAF: You're right, we did. Do you want it built here?

SOAPY: No, over there by the ash-pile. I like to be quiet.

HARALD: Right, I'll put three men on building that and the rest can start on the boat-house.

SOAPY: Sorry, you mean the wash-house, don't you?

HARALD
OLAF } : Wash-house?

HARALD: Wash-house! What are you talking about, Softy?

OLAF: His name's Soapy.

HARALD: Same thing: soft soap. We voted for a boat-house!

OLAF: He's right, Soapy. You can't argue about that.

SOAPY: There's nothing to argue about. (*Opening the book*) Look: it says in black and white it was agreed to build a wash-house, not a boat-house. Seven votes to five.

HARALD: Well, I counted, and I'll swear that more voted for a boat-house.

OLAF: Me too. Mind you, we'd had a couple of jars.

HARALD: A couple! You'd had ten at least!

OLAF: Never in this world! Six is my limit!

HARALD: You had ten! I know, 'cause you made me buy 'em!

OLAF: Are you saying I can't count? I had no more than eight!

HARALD: Ten!

They stand glaring at each other. SOAPY *laughs and puts his hands on their shoulders.*

SOAPY: Doesn't this just show how easy it is to get figures mixed up if you don't write them down? Would you like me to organise the building of the wash-house? I'm good at figures.

HARALD: We can handle that, Soapy! You're only our clerk! Come on, Olaf!

OLAF and HARALD march out. SOAPY *looks after them and grins, then starts to leave.*

KATI (*off*): Soapy! Sir! Wait a minute!

Enter the WOMEN *led by* KATI *and* LIV *carrying a bundle.*
They step forward, and the OTHER WOMEN *applaud.*

KATI: Reverend Soapy, all us women would like to thank you for
getting a wash-house started. And we all pray that we shall soon
be washing our clothes there in Thoril!

WOMEN (*clapping*): Hear, hear!

LIV: And as a sign of our gratitude, we would like to present you
with something that we have made!

She and LIV *hold up a splendid robe.* ALL *gasp or scream in delight
as* LIV *and* KATI *put it on* SOAPY. *Applause.*

WOMEN: Speech!

SOAPY: A big, big thank you to all of you! Every time that I put
on this splendid robe I shall think of you wonderful ladies!

WOMEN: Aw!

SOAPY: Please leave me now, as I would like to offer up a silent
prayer of thankfulness.

The WOMEN *applaud, then hurry out quietly except for* BRIGID
and JENNI, *who hide near the exit.* SOAPY *laughs to himself,
stroking the robe, then he puts on a pair of dark glasses and turns to
address the audience.*

SOAPY: The kids all called me Soapy,
            They thought that I was dopy,
            They said I was a real dead loss.
            Now the men all gasp in wonder
            And they have to knuckle under
            'Cause this book makes me the boss!
            The future's looking fine
            And it's all in the laws.
            (Some of 'em are mine
            And some of 'em are Thor's)
            I'll soon be in the money
            And I'll live on wine and honey
            'Cause the women can't see I'm a fake.

I'm starting up a racket
Selling powder by the packet
At ten times what it costs me to make!
I'm a cat that's tasted cream
And I'm greedy for more,
'Cause it's a living dream
To be a priest of Thor!

SOAPY *goes out. The* MEN *and* WOMEN *march on chanting* 'Hup, hup, hup!' *They line up and chant:*

MEN: We used to quarrel and bicker and squabble
For weeks and weeks and weeks.
We couldn't agree on the smallest thing,
Like where to build or what to sing
Or what to put in the fields in Spring
Or who was allowed to speak.

WOMEN: Then Soapy came to point the way
And get us off the hook.
No need to argue now because
The truths and rules and minutes and laws
Are all in Soapy's book!

MEN: The wash-house walls are going up!
It's cheered the girls no end.

WOMEN: That's right!

MEN: And then we'll build a boat-house.

BIORN: But what about the goat-house?

ALL: Forget about the goat-house!
Soapy's our guide and our friend!

ALL *applaud. A bell tolls off-stage.*

HARALD: It's Thorsday: two weeks since the Reverend Soapy
arrived! Can we finish the wash-house today, fellers?

MEN: You bet!

WOMEN: Hurray!

HARALD: And then the extension to the manse! Men, at the
double to the timber pile! Hup, hup, hup!

The MEN *run out chanting 'Hup, hup, hup!' Enter* SOAPY, *carrying the minute-book and copies of the laws.*

SOAPY: May Thor be with you!

WOMEN: And with thee.

SOAPY: Sit where you like while I read you a few more of the wonderful laws of Thor. And what's the response?

WOMEN: May the laws of Thor be written in our hearts.

SOAPY: Come on, ladies: we can do better than that! Again!

WOMEN (*loud*): May the laws of Thor be written in our hearts!

SOAPY: That's the way I like to hear it! Last week I read you the first four laws, and the fifth law is 'Thou shalt worship Thor every Thursday in the church that thou shalt build, and thou shalt give offerings to the priest of Thor.'

WOMEN: May the laws of Thor be written in our hearts!

SOAPY: Law Six: 'In Thor's eyes, all women are equal.'

BRIGID: Equal with who?

SOAPY: Sorry, that's all we have time for, but before we part, all stand and sing Thor's song while I hand out free copies of all the laws. All together: One, two!

SOAPY *hands out copies of the laws while* ALL *chant*:

ALL (*chanting*): In our sleep and in our waking
　　　　　　　　Let us worship mighty Thor.
　　　　　　　　Bring him cash and clothes and baking:
　　　　　　　　Giving is what living's for!

SOAPY: Splendid! We'll meet again next Thorsday for friendly chat, a spot of singing and some great new laws. And remember what the song says: Thor loves gifts, so if you want good weather for your washing–day, why not bring him a present?

SOME WOMEN *come forward with gifts.*

SOAPY: Thank you, thank you! Now I must go and, er, pray. And give your menfolk copies of the laws! 'Bye for now!

WOMEN: 'Bye!

Exit SOAPY. *The* WOMEN *read the laws.*

INGRID: Hey, look at Number Ten! The men'll go spare.
WOMEN (*smiling*): Right!

Enter OLAF.

OLAF: Have you women nothing to do?
WOMEN (*smiling and holding up the law*): Yes, we have!
OLAF: Well, do it! Fast!

The WOMEN *give squeals of mock alarm and hurry out, leaving* OLAF *and* INGRID.

OLAF: What are all you women reading?
INGRID: Oh, just laws.
OLAF: Laws! Any new ones?
INGRID: Just one. (*Reading*) 'Law Ten: For a whiter-than-white no-boil wash thou shalt use only New Formula Thoril, obtainable from all leading priests. Cursed be she who useth not Thoril.' There!
OLAF: Are you telling me that's a law?
INGRID: Yes, 'cause it's written down here.
OLAF: Well, why is this Thoril stuff so special?
INGRID: It contains the miracle ingredient Thorex.
OLAF: The what?
INGRID (*pointing to the paper*): 'The Miracle Ingredient Thorex, as advertised on T.V.'.
OLAF: And what the heck's T.V.?
INGRID: I'm not sure. Perhaps it means Top Value. Anyway, it's a lot better than those grotty old blocks of soap we use now. And you're always whinging about your clothes feeling greasy!
OLAF (*annoyed*): All right, why don't you use this stuff, then?
INGRID (*shouting*): Because it costs money, and I have none!
OLAF (*shouting*): Well, you're getting none from me!
INGRID: But this new law says we have to use Thoril! All of us! Or we'll be cursed!

The WOMEN *appear, listening.*

OLAF: That's your problem! You're not having my money, and that's that!

OLAF *storms off. The* WOMEN *cross to* INGRID.

INGRID: Are your men the same?
WOMEN: Worse.
INGRID: Well, are we going back to old-fashioned soap?
WOMEN: No way!
HELGA: They all want clean clothes, but they're too mean to pay!
WOMEN: Right!
ISLA: I say, we all have a right to housekeeping money!
WOMEN: Hear, hear!
ISLA: Well, follow me and we'll get some. This is what we'll do . . .

The WOMEN *go out listening to* ISLA. *The sound of hammering. The* MEN *march in carrying wood.*

MEN: When we started Soapy's house
We thought we'd soon be ended.
But he says he needs a place with lots of space
So it's got to be extended!
But we don't mind 'cause we were blind
Till Soapy opened our eyes.
A bloke so brainy needs acres of room
For all his ideas to spread and to bloom,
'Cause Soapy's amazingly wise!
BIORN: Yeah, he's clever, is Soapy!
HARALD: Oh, he's clever, all right, but . . .
MEN: But what?
HARALD: Oh, forget it. Let's get working!

The MEN *march out. More hammering. Enter the* WOMEN, *all carrying packets of Thoril.*

WOMEN (*swaying*): If your shirt is covered in dirt,
Use Thoril!

If you've got a filthy jacket
Then you need to get a packet
Of Thoril!
And if you've got a stubborn stain,
No need to rub that stain in vain,
No need to suffer or complain:
Use Thoril!

ALL except KARIN and HILDA go out chatting.

KARIN: We shouldn't have done it: it's against the law!
HILDA: How can it be? The law says we have to use Thoril.
  Come on!

They hurry out. A whistle blows off-stage and a man's voice shouts 'Find the thief!' All the MEN take up the chant. They all (except OLAF) march on stage chanting louder and louder, ending with a shout. The WOMEN run in.

INGRID: What's wrong?
OTTO: Thieving is wrong! We have a thief among us!
HILDA: And what has he been stealing?
OTTO: Money! Every man here has had money stolen from his
  jacket. Right, lads?
MEN: Right!
GAML: And we're going to find the thief and punish him!
BENNI: Or her.
ISLA: No, it can't be one of us 'cause we've all been doing our
  washing, haven't we, girls?
WOMEN: Yes, we have! So there!
ULRIC (*looking round*): Well, there's only one man missing – the
  priest!
KARIN: No, it isn't him!
OTTO: How do you know?
KARIN: Because . . . Because he's so clever.
SWAIN: Yes, he's too clever by half! Where's he hiding?
WOMEN: He's praying!

ERIK: Yes, you say he's praying, but we say he's sneaking around and stealing!

LIV: He is not! Our priest does not steal, does he?

WOMEN: No!

FINN: Well, where does he get his posh robes from?

MEN: Yeah!

KATI: He gets 'em from us, 'cause we've woven 'em and embroidered 'em in our own time!

FRITH: Well, you didn't make gold ornaments for him, did you? So where did he get them?

Enter SOAPY *carrying his bag. He starts to cross the stage.*

OTTO: There he is!

SOAPY: Thor be with you!

WOMEN: And with you, your reverence.

MEN (*blocking* SOAPY*'s way*): Stop!

SOAPY: Are you speaking to me?

IVAR: Yes, we are. Where are you going?

SOAPY: To pray. Anything else you want to know?

IVAR: Yes! What's in that bag?

SOAPY: That's my business.

ERIK: Yes, thieving's your business!

SOAPY: Do you dare call the priest of Thor a thief?

MEN: Yes!

WOMEN: No!

MEN: He is!

WOMEN: He is not!

Enter OLAF. *Silence.*

OLAF: What's all this shouting? You should be at work.

HARALD: We've all had money stolen, and we accuse the priest!

MEN: Yes!

OLAF (*to* SOAPY): What do you say?

SOAPY: I say, let me prove my innocence.

WOMEN: Yes, let him prove it!

OLAF *holds up a hand.* ALL *freeze.* OLAF *comes forward.*

OLAF (*to the audience*): According to Viking tradition, there are
three ways to prove your innocence of theft: you can carry red-
hot iron for ten paces, or you can fish a heavy stone out of
boiling water, or you can open the bag. And just over there is a
fire with the red-hot iron and the boiling water. (*To the
OTHERS*) What should he do?
BIORN: Carry the red-hot iron!
SOME MEN: Yeah!
IVAR: Plunge his hands in boiling water!
OTHER MEN: Yeah!
KARIN: Choose the water, Soapy!
ANNI: No, go for the iron!

Shouts and yells build up as ALL *encourage* SOAPY *to choose
either the fire or the iron.*

OLAF (*raising his hand*): Quiet! (*To* SOAPY) Have you made your
choice?
SOAPY: Yes, I have.

Cheers and applause.

OLAF (*to the audience*): So Soapy has made his choice! (*To*
SOAPY) And what have you chosen? Is it the red-hot iron or
the boiling water?
SOAPY: Neither: I'll open the bag!
ALL: Aw!
OTTO: Chicken!
OLAF: Silence! He's within his rights! He's chosen to open the bag
to prove that he's not a thief. Ulric, would you step forward
and show us what's in the bag!

Applause. SOAPY *gives the bag to* ULRIC, *who starts taking
objects out and holding them up.*

ULRIC: Number One: a minute-book, labelled, er . . .
SOAPY: Please return to the priest of Thor.

ULRIC: Please return to the priest of Thor.

Applause.

ULRIC (*taking out a whisky-bottle and sniffing it*): Number Two: a
   bottle of, er . . .
SOAPY: Holy water.
ULRIC: It doesn't smell holy to me.
OLAF: Carry on.
ULRIC: Number Three: a packet of New Formula Super Thoril.

Applause.

ULRIC: Fourthly and lastly, a purse containing (*opening it*) twenty
   five silver coins!
MEN: Twenty five silver coins!
MAGNUS: Where did he get all that money?
OTTO: He stole it!
MEN: Yeah, he stole it!
BIORN: He's the thief!
MEN: Thief! Thief! Thief!
SOAPY: I am not a thief!
MAGNUS: So where did you get that money?
MEN: Yes, where?

   The WOMEN *step forward in a group.*

LIV: From us!
MEN: From you?
WOMEN: Yes, us!
FREDA: We gave him that money to pay for packets of Thoril.
GAML: But that's our money! We've earned it, selling what we've
   grown and caught!
FREDA: And haven't we earned it? Cooking and cleaning and
   washing and weaving and spinning and mending and . . .
ERIK: All right, but we didn't give it to you.
INGRID: No, so we took it!
WOMEN: Yes!
MAGNUS: So you're the thieves!

MEN: Yeah!

MAGNUS (*to* SOAPY): I'm sorry we accused you: it's the women who have to be punished.

SOAPY: We all make mistakes.

OLAF: So how shall we punish the women?

BIORN (*raising a hand*): Fine 'em a lot of money!

The MEN *groan and the* WOMEN *laugh mockingly.*

IVAR: They haven't got any money, have they, stupid?

BIORN: Oh no, I forgot.

OTTO: I say, burn their hands!

MEN: Yeah! Burn their hands!

HELGA: Brilliant! Then we can't do any housework!

ISLA: Burn me now, please, then I don't have to cook!

WOMEN (*holding up their hands*): And me! Me, please! Burn me!

OLAF: Shut up! We're not going to burn you!

WOMEN: Aw!

MAGNUS: Well, we can't just let 'em go scot-free.

FRITH: What do the laws of Thor say about punishments for stealing?

SOAPY (*looking in his book*): Er, punishments for stealing. Er, imprisonment, fines, burning, hanging . . . Ah! 'If the punishment is in doubt, the courtfolk shall ask Thor for guidance.'

OLAF: Right, how do we ask Thor?

SOAPY (*consulting his book*): Er, 'All shall kneel.'

ALL *kneel except* SOAPY, JENNI *and* BRIGID.

SOAPY: Why don't you two kneel?

BRIGID ⎫
JENNI ⎭ : Why don't you?

SOAPY: Er, because it says here: 'All present shall kneel *except the priest of Thor*'.

JENNI: Let's see it.

ALL: Kneel down!

JENNI: I just want to see . . .

ALL: Shut up and kneel down!

BRIGID ⎱
JENNI ⎰ (*kneeling*): Don't say we didn't warn you!

SOAPY (*reading*): 'All present except the priest of Thor shall kneel and place before them all gold, silver and other valuables'.

> ALL *reach for their valuables, then hesitate.*

SWAIN: Why does it say that?

SOAPY: Because Thor cannot communicate with us if our thought-rays are blocked by precious metals.

BENNI (*putting down an armlet*): That sounds like sense.

ALL: Yes, that's right.

> ALL *look at each other, then one after another they put down their valuables.*

SOAPY (*to* ULRIC): Where's your lucky gold hammer?

> ULRIC *shrugs, fishes out a gold medallion and puts it down.*

SOAPY (*reading*): 'All except the priest shall close their eyes while Thor speaks'.

OLAF: Eyes closed. No cheating.

> ALL *except* SOAPY, JENNI *and* BRIGID *close their eyes.*

SOAPY: The eyes of thy servants are closed, O Thor!

> As he speaks, SOAPY *takes a sheet of metal from the wings.* BRIGID *and* JENNI *pocket their valuables.*

SOAPY: Speak, O Thor! Speak in a voice of thunder!

> He suddenly shakes the thunder-sheet. ALL *exclaim.*

SOAPY: Speak again, O Thor!

> SOAPY *continues to call* 'Speak, O Thor!' *and shake the sheet while scooping up the valuables and dropping them in his bag. Then he*

goes to the exit, puts down the sheet, blows a kiss to them all and hurries off. BRIGID *and* JENNI *laugh silently*

OLAF: What does he say, Soapy? (*Looking round*) Soapy!

ALL *open their eyes and look round, blinking. One after another they stand.* BRIGID *and* JENNI *laugh aloud.*

OLAF (*calling*): Soapy! (*To* BRIGID *and* JENNI) What are you two laughing at?

HARALD: He's gone!

BIORN: So has my money.

KATI: And all our ornaments!

BENNI: Perhaps Thor's taken them.

BRIGID: And perhaps Soapy has.

ALL: Oh, no!

BRIGID ⎫
JENNI ⎭ : Oh, yes!

ULRIC: Where's my good-luck hammer?

JENNI: Soapy's taken it: for good!

Laughter.

FINN (*shaking the thunder-sheet*): And here's the voice of Thor.

IVAR: He was a thief and a liar all along!

BENNI: Yes! I say, hanging's too good for him!

ALL: Hear, hear!

OTTO: We'll cut his hands off, then we'll hang him!

ALL: Right!

BRIGID: You need to catch him first!

OLAF: Saddle the horses!

BRIGID: Horses are no good! Look: he's rowing across the river!

OLAF: Launch a boat!

The MEN *run off, shouting instructions to each other.* JENNI *and* BRIGID *put their ornaments back on.*

LIV: Hey, how come he didn't get your things?

JENNI: 'Cause we didn't trust him. We had a look through his
  window last night, and what do you think he was doing?

KARIN
ISLA } : Praying.

BRIGID
JENNI } (*laughing*): Praying!

KARIN: Well, what was he doing?

JENNI: Snoring over an empty whisky bottle.

GUDRUN: I thought that bottle wasn't holy water!

ISLA: And he said he never drank, didn't he?

ALL: That's right.

  The MEN *run back in.*

OLAF: Did you catch him?

HARALD: No, he got clean away.

ERIK: And he's taken the oars from all the other boats.

WOMEN: Aw!

BRIGID: Listen: we sneaked into Soapy's house last night and had
  a look round. (*Producing* SOAPY's *certificate*) Recognise this?

BIORN: That's his certificate, isn't it? To show he's a priest, after
  all his time studying in Denmark.

BRIGID: He did time in Denmark all right. Listen to this:
  (*Reading*) 'This is to certify that Sigurd Sigurdson, commonly
  called Soapy, was duly released on the third of this month after
  serving two years' hard labour for forgery and theft. Signed,
  Prison Governor.'

ALL: Aw!

BRIGID: And at the bottom he's scribbled a recipe for making
  soap powder, using tallow and – I can't read it – and wood ash.

HILDA: Secret ingredient Thorex!

HARALD: So that's why he wanted his house by the ash-heap!

OLAF: Why did we ever trust him? We knew what he was like!

ERIK: It was all his writing that fooled me.

MEN: Mmm.

KARIN: And it was all his talking that fooled us.

WOMEN: Mmm. He spoke so nicely.

KARIN: He called us ladies, didn't he?

WOMEN: Mmm: ladies.

GAML: So he just soft-soaped you all, did he?

HILDA: He took us all in, men and women.

JENNI: Most of us.

IVAR: And he took most of our valuables.

ALL: Right!

GUDRUN: Well, look on the bright side: we know how to make soap powder.

HELGA: And he got us a new wash-house.

OTTO: Hey, what say we build that boat-house before the bad weather sets in?

ULRIC: Good idea!

BIORN: No, I'm sick of building!

MAGNUS: Hear, hear!

> *Soon,* ALL *except* OLAF *are squabbling.*

OLAF: Shut up!

> *Instant silence.*

OLAF: We've got to learn from all this! We've got to start discussing things properly without squabbling and shouting! All of us! Right?

ALL: Right!

BRIGID: Does 'All of us' include women?

BIORN: No! Women aren't clever enough.

JENNI: Oh yes, bright boy? How many of you men saw through Soapy?

BRIGID: Come on, chaps, will you give us the vote?

> *The* MEN *look at each other and nod.*

OLAF: All right: from now on, women can speak and vote at meetings.

> *The* WOMEN *cheer.*

HELGA: So now we can discuss things in a civilised way.

OLGA: Let's have a meeting now!
WOMEN: Yes!

The WOMEN *grab the seats and sit. The* MEN *except* OLAF *roll their eyes and stand.*

OLAF: Right, what do you want to discuss in a civilised way?
HELGA (*raising a hand*): All housewives should be paid!
WOMEN: Hear, hear!
MEN: Rubbish!
WOMEN: Why is it rubbish?
KATI: Write it down! Somebody write it down!
OLAF: Order! Order!

But ALL *have begun to squabble loudly, with* OLAF *trying to bring them to order as the curtain closes. When it opens again for the curtain-call,* SOAPY *steps forward to speak the Epilogue:*

Epilogue
SOAPY: What is written may be true,
Telling people what to do,
Giving you a task.
But before you do it,
There's a question you should ask:
Who wrote it? Whose pen was in the ink?
Is he fair as people think?
And consider for a minute
Just exactly what is in it
For the hand that wrote the rule.
And don't be made a fool.
ALL: And don't be made a fool!
Good night!

(*Curtain*)

SELL-OUT

CHARACTERS

DICK WHITTINGTON
CAT/FELICITY, *his sister*
BILLIE ⎫
⎬ *U.S. tourists*
BOBBIE ⎭
COUNCILLOR PURSLOVE

Peasants
ADAM
ANNA
BESS
EDNA
HANS
JACK
JANE
JESS
JUDE
LILY
MARY
MIKE
NORA
PHIL
WYNN

PLACE: The Village Green in Pantoville, on the outskirts of London.
TIME: At first, the Peasants are living in the past and the others in the present. By the end, everyone is living in the present.

Staging

The usual entrance (the road to London) is downstage on the actors' left (D.L.), and the way from the country is on the opposite side (D.R.) by the milestone. It probably works best if the well is upstage, right of centre (U.R.C.). If it's easier for you, reverse these directions, of course.

Scene 1

*The Village Green of Pantoville. A suggestion of pantomime cottages·
small, quaint, brickbuilt, with latticed windows, painted hollyhocks and
roses round the door. A milestone saying 'LONDON 3 miles' stands
D.R.. Upstage of it, a picturesque well. Near it, a bench or block.*

  *Enter D.L., BILLIE, an American tourist wearing a Stetson, hung
with cameras and equipment and holding a guidebook.*

BILLIE (*seeing the cottages*): Wow! (*Calling*) Hey, Bobbie!

BOBBIE (*off, shrill*): Whaaat?

BILLIE: Come and get an eyeful of this: it's another world! Oldie-
  Worldie English Cottages!

BOBBIE (*off*): Whaaat? (*Entering, similarly clad and equipped, seeing
  the cottages*) Hey, ain't that something else? (*Taking pictures*) Wait
  till the folks back home in the States see these pictures! What is
  this place, anyway?

BILLIE (*consulting the guidebook*): Looks like it's Pantoville.

BOBBIE: Pantoville. Is it famous, like Stratford and Edinburg-on-
  Avon?

BILLIE: I don't know, but it says here 'Picturesque Pantoville has
  remained unchanged for over four hundred years'.

BOBBIE: Four hundred??

BILLIE: Yup! Listen! (*Reading*) 'Over the years, Pantoville has
  been the setting for many of London's famed pantomimes, and
  the friendly inhabitants are justly proud of taking part in the
  chorus, just like their forefathers before them.'

  HANS *and* LILY *enter upstage carrying plastic buckets. Like all the*
  PEASANTS, *their clothes are vaguely mediaeval, brightly coloured,
  with large square contrasting patches. Scowling, they cross to the well.*

BOBBIE (*pointing and focusing*): Hey, friendly inhabitants!

LILY (*getting water*): And another thing, why can't I have new
  clothes?

HANS: Because panto-ing doesn't pay well enough, that's why!

LILY: Look at these stupid patches!

HANS: They're traditional!

LILY: Well, I'm sick of 'em, and this traditional flaming well, as well!

HANS: Well . . .

They are shouting and glaring now. BOBBIE *approaches them.*

BOBBIE: Pardon me . . .

Instantly they turn to face BOBBIE *with broad smiles pasted on their faces. Like all Pantoville folk, they keep these smiles whenever strangers are around.*

HANS ⎱ : Good morning! Welcome to Pantoville! Can we help
LILY ⎰   you?

BOBBIE: I wonder, could you move nearer to the . . . ?

HANS ⎱ : Of course!
LILY ⎰

They move quickly to the well and pose by it, still smiling. They've obviously done this often before.

BILLIE: Pardon me, I couldn't help overhearing you two quarrelling . . .

LILY (*still smiling*): We never quarrel!

HANS: Everyone's happy in Pantoville!

BILLIE: Oh, my mistake: sorry.

HANS: That's all right!

BOBBIE (*finishing snapping*): Thank you.

LILY ⎱ : Thank *you.*
HANS ⎰

    HANS *and* LILY *start to draw water. Enter* MARY *with buckets and sees them.*

MARY: Not you two here again! Every bleeding morning!

    HANS *and* LILY *indicate the* TOURISTS. MARY *instantly changes, smiling like the others.*

MARY (*to* BILLIE *and* BOBBIE): Good morning! Welcome to
Pantoville! Can I help you?

*She poses by the well. BILLIE shrugs and takes a picture. A bell
starts ringing quickly. Instantly the stage is filled with merry
PEASANTS carrying buckets. They line up facing the audience.
BOBBIE and BILLIE move D.L. as they sing with appropriate
gestures:*

The Land of Pantomime

The sun is shining in the blue, the birds are singing in the trees,
The flowers in the gardens are blowing in the breeze.
The windmill sails are turning and the merry church-bells chime,
And life is grand throughout the land, the land of Pantomime.

It never snows, it never rains, the weather's always bright,
There's no litter or graffiti, and everyone's polite.
We may be short of money, but we've never heard of crime,
And dreams come true for you and you in the land of Pantomime.

So, our hearts are full of merriment, a smile on every face:
We love to sing, we love to dance: we're happy in our place.
It's so pleasant being a peasant that we never want to climb
Any higher up the ladder in the land of Pantomime!

*They finish with arms outflung. BILLIE and BOBBIE clap.
MIKE approaches with a bucket, and they drop money in.*

MIKE: Thank you! Thank you! Isn't it a grand morning!
BILLIE: What's the collection for?
MIKE: For the water fund, sir.
BOBBIE: What's that?

The PEASANTS gather round.

ADAM: To bring us piped water, so we don't have to queue at the
well every day.
BOBBIE: You mean, there's no running water in these houses?
BESS: Oh, yes! It runs down all the walls: isn't that right?
PEASANTS: That's right! But no taps!

BILLIE: So you've no, er, toilet facilities either?

ANNA: We all have a loo at the bottom of the garden: want to see one?

BILLIE: No, no!

BOBBIE: This is terrible! Why doesn't the council make your landlord fix your houses?

PEASANTS (*laughing*): The council!

JESS: Because we all live in tied council cottages.

BOBBIE: What's a tied cottage?

JUDE: It's a cottage that's tied to the job, so we only have one as long as we work for the council.

MARY: I lie awake worrying.

PHIL: We only pay low rents, though.

BESS: Yes, because we all have such a low-paid job!

PEASANTS: That's right!

BILLIE: Doing what?

ANNA: We all work as Pleasant Peasants.

BILLIE
BOBBIE } : Pleasant Peasants! What's that?

PHIL: Ar! I've been a Pleasant Peasant sixty years, man and beast, and I'll tell you what it means. First, we all have to wear these clothes. They're bright, to show we're happy, and patched, to show we're poor. Poverty Patches, we call 'em. Right?

PEASANTS: Right!

PHIL: Now, our job is to look happy. Like, the hero of a pantomime always comes here, right?

PEASANTS: Right!

PHIL: Like Jack, taking his cow to market, or Aladdin, or Ali Baba, or Dick Whittington seeking his fortune, or . . .

BILLIE: Okay, okay, but what do you *do*?

PEASANTS: We look happy, and we sing to 'em!

WYNN: However much they're down in the dumps – and this *is* a dump – it's our job to cheer 'em up with a smile and a song.

PEASANTS (*smiling and singing*): With a smile and a song!

BOBBIE: And what's the pay like?

PEASANTS: Terrible!

BILLIE: But you all look so happy!

JACK: Only because it's part of the job! (*Looking round*) Listen, and we'll sing you the secret part of our song. One, two!

Now Listen to the Other Side

PEASANTS:

Now listen to the other side, a side that's grim and dark,
And we'll reveal the truth about this 'Pleasant Peasant' lark.
We *have* to grin, we *have* to sing with joy and smiles abundant –
'Cos if we ever stop it then we're quickly made redundant!

Another drawback of the job that lessens our enjoyment –
There are no legal limits to our hours of employment.
We have to be on call all day and sometimes all night long
In case the hero of a show should want to sing a song.

For when a hero's down and out, and sorrow brims his cup,
He comes here to the village green for us to cheer him up.
But when he's made his fortune and his purse is full of gold,
He doesn't want to know us and he leaves us in the cold.

The council love the peasants 'cos we never ask for more,
And they say 'Oh, aren't you lucky having roses round the door?'
But each cottage is so leaky it's like living in a ditch:
Why should we dwell in poverty when other folk are rich?

BOBBIE (*dropping more money in the bucket*): We hope things'll get better some fine day.

EDNA: It might be today, 'cos it's Grant Day.

BILLIE: What's Grant Day?

EDNA: It's the day when the council announce how they're going to spend the taxpayers' money.

JANE: And we hope they're going to spend some on repairing our houses.

JESS: And raising our pay!

PEASANTS: Hear, hear!

MARY: I don't suppose they will.

PEASANTS: Nah.

MIKE: And if the council don't, no-one else will.

BOBBIE: Why not ask the King and Queen to help you?

PEASANTS: Ooh, no!

EDNA: We couldn't do that, could we, neighbours?

PEASANTS: Ooh, no!

JANE: We don't want to worry the King and Queen with our affairs, God bless 'em!

PEASANTS: God bless 'em!

A coach horn toots offstage.

BILLIE: That's our coach: off to Edinburg! We've gotta run!

BOBBIE: 'Bye! Keep smiling!

BILLIE *and* BOBBIE *hurry off. The* PEASANTS *watch them, their smiles disappearing.*

PEASANTS: 'Keep smiling'. Huh!

They drift into a queue at the well. MARY *tries to get near the head of the queue.*

JESS: Hey, why are you pushing in?

MARY: 'Cos I was one of the first here, that's why!

JUDE: Oh, yes? Says who?

MARY: Says me! Move!

JUDE: No way!

JUDE *and* MARY *start pushing each other.* OTHERS *jostle and shout encouragement. The noise rises until* WYNN, *who has been keeping watch, sees someone offstage.*

WYNN: Old Pursy! Councillor Purslove!

ALL: Councillor Purslove!

ALL *shuffle into a neat, smiling queue. Enter* COUNCILLOR PURSLOVE *with a briefcase.*

PEASANTS: Morning, Councillor! Isn't it a grand day?

COUNCILLOR: Shut up!

He mounts the block, produces a bell and rings it.

COUNCILLOR: Hear ye! Hear ye!

PEASANTS: Hear we! Hear we!

COUNCILLOR: Be quiet! (*Reading from a paper*) 'Borough of
Pantoville: annual rates and charges. As from today, all council
rents will be doubled.'

PEASANTS: Doubled!

COUNCILLOR: Quiet! 'Furthermore, to pay for the re-gilding of
the Town Hall dome, the council will cease to provide free
services, including the Pantoville Peasants' Chorus.'

ADAM: That's us!

COUNCILLOR (*stepping down*): That is correct.

NORA: Are you telling us that you're stopping our wages and
doubling our rents?

COUNCILLOR: I am.

NORA: But if we have no wages, how can we pay these rents?

PEASANTS: Yes, how?

COUNCILLOR: You'll all have to find proper jobs, won't you?
I'll be back next week, and you'd better have your rents ready
or you'll be thrown out of your cottages. Good morning!

PEASANTS: Good morning, Councillor.

He leaves, and their smiles fade.

MIKE: 'Find proper jobs!' What else can we do?

PHIL: Well, I've been a Pleasant Peasant sixty years, and . . .

ALL: Shut up!

NORA: Hey, we don't have to smile at strangers now!

ALL: That's right!

LILY: And we don't have to wear these clothes, either.

ANNA: Not if you've got something else.

BESS: And we don't have to sing, either.

WYNN: But singing's a habit. You might say it's inbred.

MIKE: It may be inbred, but there's no bread in it! (*Laughing*)

ALL (*staring*): What?

MIKE: It's a joke.

ALL (*deadpan*): Oh.

MARY: Well, telling jokes doesn't bring bread in, either. Not jokes like that, anyway. We've got to find work, fast, or we'll be out on the streets. Let's put our heads together.

ALL look at her, shrug, and huddle upstage trying to put their heads together. DICK WHITTINGTON and his CAT enter D.R.. Some OLDER PEASANTS smile automatically, but others nudge them to stop.

DICK (*seeing the milestone but not the* PEASANTS): 'London, three miles!' Soon we shall reach the city of our dreams, Puss!

PUSS miaows.

DICK: They say the streets are paved with gold. Do you believe that, Puss?

PUSS miaows.

DICK: I'm not sure that I do, either, but two things I do know. One is that I shall make my fortune somehow, even if I have to kill my grandmother, and the other is that these kind folk here (*Gesturing without looking*) will give us a smiling welcome and sing us (*Slapping his thigh*) a merry song!

Soft introductory music for 'The Land of Pantomime' begins and continues under the following:

DICK: I'm on my way to London, simple peasants.

ANNA: Less of the 'Simple'.

DICK: But first, I pray, to make the day more pleasant,
      Before we further wend upon our way
      Let's hear you sing some merry roundelay!

JESS (*coming forward*): What?

The music stops.

DICK: A merry roundelay! A song! Come, begin!

The music starts again.

JUDE (*to the musician*): Hold it, hold it, hold it! (*To* DICK) How much?

DICK: What?

JESS: How much money have you got?

DICK: Nothing. That's why we're walking to London: to seek our fortunes. Aren't we, Puss?

PUSS miaows.

DICK: Now, are you going to sing or not?

PEASANTS: No!

DICK: Why not?

ADAM: We can't afford to sing for free.

HANS: Because we need the money, see?

DICK: I thought you'd sing to cheer a stranger.

EDNA: No. It's a hard world nowadays, young man.

DICK: And aren't the streets of London paved with gold?

JACK: I've heard they're paved with litter, whatever that is.

PEASANTS: Right!

JACK: And unless you have the money, there's neither song nor sympathy for man or beast, is there, neighbours?

PEASANTS: None!

DICK: I see. Come out, Sis!

> *To gasps of amazement and applause, the* CAT *takes off its cat-suit, throwing it into the wings and revealing herself as a girl stylishly clad in jeans and top. She shakes out her long, glossy hair. The* WOMEN *whisper together.*

FELICITY: Hi there, everybody!

PEASANTS: Hi!

DICK: This is my sister, Felicity. She wants to make a fortune, too, and she thought London folk might be kinder to her if she dressed as an animal.

BESS: Excuse me, miss: all us girls are wondering how you get your hair so shiny?

FELICITY: I always use 'Head Girl' shampoo. Like in the adverts.

PEASANT WOMEN: Shampoo? What's that?

WYNN: Like champagne, perhaps.

JANE: Yes, I've heard of washing your hair in beer.

JACK: No beer round here.

PEASANTS: That's right.

ADAM: And what are adverts?

PEASANTS: Yes, what are they?

FELICITY: Everyone knows what adverts are!

JANE: We don't. We've heard of 'em, but the council don't allow 'em.

LILY: Like litter, and graffiti, whatever they are.

JACK: And beer.

NORA: And V.T., whatever that is.

DICK: V.T.? Oh, you mean T.V.?

NORA: That's right, T.V..

FELICITY: Gosh! Aren't you all ignorant?

PEASANTS: That's right, we are.

DICK: Well, we must go to London, even if the streets are only paved with litter. Are any of you going that way?

PEASANTS: Ooh, no: we daren't!

FELICITY: Why on earth not?

MIKE: We only have these clothes to wear, and if ever we venture outside Pantoville, the outside folk jeer at us.

ANNA: They laugh and throw stones at us.

BESS: So we stay here, where it's safe.

PEASANTS: That's right.

FELICITY: Tough luck! Come on, Dick: I want to see the bright lights!

She starts to go. DICK *follows her.*

DICK: Right-o, Felicity! 'Bye, peasants!

PEASANTS: 'Bye, sir!

DICK *and* FELICITY *go off towards London. The* PEASANTS *watch them go, then look at each other.*

MARY: All right for them. We'll be out on the street unless we get jobs. What are we going to do?

EDNA: We need to keep thinking about it.

PEASANTS: Right.

LILY: We may as well queue up while we think.

ALL *shuffle into line. The lights dim to indicate the passage of time. Perhaps a clock strikes.*

Scene 2

When the lights come up, the PEASANTS *are still in line, though the order has changed.*

EDNA: We seem to have been standing here a week.

PEASANTS: Right, we have.

ADAM: Here! It's rent day, and the Councillor'll be round soon to evict us unless we pay him.

MARY: I said last week we needed to get jobs!

HANS: Saying doesn't help, does it?

WYNN: I can't believe the council 'ud throw us out after all these years.

JESS: I hear they want to get us out so they can gentrify our cottages for these here Yuppies.

JUDE: What's a Yuppy?

JESS: Sort of fish, I think.

PHIL: Nah, it's a rich young gent, like.

JACK: Remember that young gent and his sister, last week?

MIKE: Right. Adverts, she talked about. What are they?

PEASANTS: Don't know, don't care.

Rock music is heard from the direction of London. ALL *turn to stare. It gets louder.* DICK *and* FELICITY *enter, wearing dark glasses and new jackets.* DICK *carries a film camera,* FELICITY *wears earphones and carries a microphone on a boom and a portable control-panel-cum-radio. She switches the music off.*

DICK (*looking round*): Here we are again: out of this world!

DICK paces out a few steps, turns, walks back and peers through a view-finder while FELICITY *adjusts the controls and says 'Testing, testing, testing'. The* PEASANTS *stare.*

JANE: Excuse me, miss: what are you doing?

FELICITY: I'm testing, sweety.

JANE (*to the* OTHERS): She's testing, sweety!

PEASANTS (*nodding wisely*): Ah! Testing sweety!

ANNA: And might we ask what you're doing, Mr Whittington?

DICK: Making commercials.

PEASANTS (*nodding and smiling*): Ah, commercials! (*Their smiles fade*) What are commercials?

DICK: Could some of your people bring that trolley on? (*Gesturing*)

> Some PEASANTS *hurry into the wings and bring on a trolley piled with crates of green, brown and clear bottles, all with large, impressive labels. The* OTHER PEASANTS *clap.*

DICK: We're making three commercials about the magic liquids in these bottles.

PEASANTS: Magic liquids! Fancy that!

DICK: But we need extra bodies.

> DICK *looks round as if puzzled. So do the* PEASANTS.

FELICITY: Dick!

DICK: Yes, Felicity?

FELICITY: I wonder if these good people could help?

DICK: No, we must have *singers*, Felicity!

ADAM: We can sing, sir! Can't we, folks?

PEASANTS: 'Course we can!

FELICITY: Ah, but can you all give great big smiles?

> The PEASANTS *all grin manically.*

DICK: Brilliant! But can you all sing and smile at the same time?

JACK: One, two!

PEASANTS (*Singing*): The sun is shining in the blue, the birds . . .

DICK: Marvellous! Brilliant! Wonderful! When can you start?

PEASANTS: Now!

DICK: Super! First, we'll take 'Head Girl'.

PEASANTS: Head Girl!

JESS: Excuse me, Mr Whittington.

DICK: Yes?

JESS: How much are you paying for this job?

FELICITY: This isn't a job: it's an experience!

JUDE: All right. How much are you paying us for this experience?

HANS: Because the minimum wage . . .

DICK (*pushing him*): Don't use words like 'Minimum wage' to my sister! Do you want to help or not?

HANS
JUDE } : Well, erm . . .
JESS

WYNN: Yes, we do! Don't we, folks?

PEASANTS: Yes, we do!

FELICITY: Oh, let's get on with it before the light goes!

DICK: Right! Who are the girls with the glossiest hair?

FELICITY *rapidly selects them and arranges them.*

DICK: Super! Green bottles!

PEASANTS *hurry to get green bottles, and distribute them.*

DICK: Great! Follow the autocue on the camera!

FELICITY: Sound running!

DICK: Action!

FELICITY *holds up a clapperboard which says 'Head Girl. Director: R. Whittington. Take 1' The chosen* GIRLS *stand and sing to the camera, with the* OTHERS *surrounding them and holding up their bottles.*

Head Girl

GIRLS: I used to be an ordinary girl,
> The sort of girl that fellers pass by.
> > As I walked along the street
> > I was cool and I was neat,
> But I never caught anybody's eye.

Then Head Girl came on the market:
I decided to give it a whirl,
   For I hadn't been aware
   Of my dull and greasy hair –
And now I am a very different girl!

'Cos every time I walk along the street
I'm a magnet for everybody's eye!
   Fellers' lips are licking
   And their cameras are clicking
And I hold my head up high!

For Head Girl makes me radiant!
There's magic in that bottle so green!
   My hair's my crowning glory
   And my life's a fairy story,
And people say 'She must be a queen!'

Yes, I'm a queen! Thanks to Head Girl, I feel like a queen!
Head Girl!

DICK (*applauding*): That was fantastic! You're all naturals! But just to make sure, let's have a second take of the last verse. Singers, swing those hips more, and on the last line stretch out those arms! Everyone else, hold that smile and keep your bottle up! O.K.? Stand by!

   FELICITY *holds up the clapperboard, which now says 'Take 2'.*

DICK: Action!

   They sing the last verse again. FELICITY *applauds.*

DICK: My sister likes it! You've made a hit! What's next, Felicity?
FELICITY: Next is the new friendly drink called Cheer. Brown bottles.

   Laughing and chattering, the PEASANTS *quickly change bottles. This time it's mainly the macho men who face the camera.*

DICK: Right, drinkers! (*He claps to quieten them*) Thank you! Labels facing the camera, one step forward at the end of each verse, and everyone – that means everyone – shouts 'Cheer!' Then, right at the end, 'Cheer and cheer and cheer! Three cheers!' O.K.?

FELICITY: Could I hear the end to check the sound levels?

DICK: Of course you can, sweety! End of the last verse, and everybody join in on 'And cheer' One, two!

SINGERS (MEN): You'll fly higher than a kite:
                    You'll feel like a king tonight,

ALL: And cheer and cheer and cheer!
                    Three cheers!

FELICITY *gives* DICK *a thumbs-up.*

DICK: Fantastic: we're going for a take. Stand by. From the top.

FELICITY: Sound running.

DICK: Smile! Action!

FELICITY *snaps the clapperboard, which now says 'Cheer. Take 1'. The chosen* MEN *sing*:

Cheer

MEN: You've all seen it advertised:
      The drink that tastes of paradise –
      The stuff that's known as

ALL: Cheer!

MEN: Why not march into the bar
      Where the biggest boozers are
      And ask for a pint of

ALL: Cheer!

MEN: Like the fellers on the telly,
      Soon you'll have a swelling belly,
      Stomachs full of

ALL: Cheer!

MEN: Once your guts are blown up tight
      You can sing and you can fight.
      You'll fly higher than a kite:
      You'll feel like a king tonight,

ALL: And cheer and cheer and cheer!
         Three cheers!

They stay frozen in their smile.

DICK: O.K., Felicity? (*She nods*) Well done! Relax! Now, our last
    masterpiece is another drink. I've never enjoyed it, but it can
    cost the earth, and it's called Loyalty. Yes, Loyalty! Let's use the
    folk who haven't featured yet. Clear bottles this time.

The chosen singers get clear bottles, and FELICITY *gives* ALL *a
small Union Jack.*

DICK: Stand together, Loyalists! Everyone else stand at the back.
    Wave your flags and shout 'That's Loyalty!' after the last three
    verses. Let's hear it for Felicity: 'That's Loyalty!'
PEASANTS: That's Loyalty!
FELICITY: Louder!
PEASANTS: That's Loyalty!

FELICITY *gives* DICK *a thumbs-up.*

DICK: Great! Going for a take! Stand by!
FELICITY: Sound running!
DICK: Action!

FELICITY *snaps the clapperboard, which says 'Loyalty. Take 1'.*

SINGERS: We're only common working-class:
              Just peasants and their wives,
              And every day drags on the same –
              No colour in our lives.
              Then one fine day the Prince was crowned –
              We saw the Coronation,
              And we were filled with Loyalty
              For the rulers of our nation!
jANE: Sixty pictures of the King in our house!
NORA: And a letter from the Queen in ours!
EDNA: I confess that ever since I nearly met the Prince
              I dream of him for hours!

ALL: That's Loyalty!

SINGERS: When the new Princess has a baby,
            We'll all send gifts to the Court.
            Every pound we have to spare will go to her son and heir
            So the poor mite won't go short!

ALL: That's Loyalty!

SINGERS: We still live in poverty,
            We have no cause to smile,
            But poverty there's not, aboard the Royal Yacht –
            And that makes it all worthwhile!

ALL: That's Loyalty!

DICK *and* FELICITY *do a thumbs-up to each other and applaud.*
The PEASANTS *bow.* DICK *and* FELICITY *move apart.*

FELICITY ⎫
DICK   ⎬ : It's in the can! Whee! (*Embracing*)

DICK: We're in the big money!

FELICITY: Millions! What about these stupid peasants?

DICK: I'll sort 'em out.

DICK *crosses to the* PEASANTS *while* FELICITY *packs up.*

DICK: Did you enjoy that?

PEASANTS: Yes!!

DICK: Splendid! My partner and I would like to thank you all very, very much for being such charming and helpful folk.

ADAM: And thank you, sir, for letting us help you.

PEASANTS: Hear, hear!

EDNA: And I'd like to apologise, sir, for those greedy trouble-makers who wanted paying.

DICK: I'm afraid there are greedy people everywhere, aren't there?

PEASANTS: That's right.

DICK: Now, we're working to a very tight budget, but we've agreed that you can keep those valuable flags you're holding.

JANE: Oh, God bless you, sir!

PEASANTS: Hear, hear!

FELICITY: And the bottles!

DICK: What?

FELICITY: They can have the bottles: they're worthless . . . Er, worth so much.

DICK: Hear that, folks? All those valuable bottles are yours as well!

WYNN: Four cheers for Master Richard and Miss Felicity! May fame and fortune attend them! Hip, hip!

PEASANTS: Hurray!

WYNN: Hip, hip, hip!

PEASANTS: Hurray! Hurray!

WYNN: Hip, hip, hip, hip!

PEASANTS: Hurray! Hurray! Hurray! Hurray! (*Waving frantically*)

FELICITY: Thank you all. Now, we have business to attend to, as I'm sure you do. 'Bye, everybody!

DICK: 'Bye!

PEASANTS: 'Bye! 'Bye!

The PEASANTS *continue shouting and waving as* DICK *and* FELICITY *go out, then gradually they fall still.*

EDNA: Isn't she lovely? Like a Princess.

WOMEN: Mmm.

PHIL: And he's a grand young man: I hope he makes his fortune.

ALL: Right!

ANNA: Never mind about them: what about us? Councillor Purslove'll be here soon, wanting our rent. Can anybody pay him?

PEASANTS (*looking at each other*): No.

BESS: What can we do?

JACK: I know what I'm going to do: I'm going to cheer myself up. (*Getting a brown bottle and reading the label*) It says here 'The drink that's guaranteed to make you feel well'. Good health!

He opens the bottle, takes a drink, smiles, looks uncertain and sniffs the contents.

MIKE: What's wrong?

JACK: I don't know. Here. (*Giving* MIKE *the bottle*)

MIKE (*taking a swig and also looking puzzled*): It's familiar.

JESS (*grabbing the bottle and tasting*): I'll tell you what this stuff is: it's well-water!

ALL: Well-water?

JUDE: Right! (*Inspecting the label*) 'Makes you feel well'. (*Mocking*) Ha, ha!

BESS: You reckon all these bottles are full of well-water?

LILY: Could be. (*Inspecting a bottle of Loyalty*) 'Loyalty: the drink that fills you with well-being'.

ALL: Well-being!

LILY: They can say that again! What's the shampoo say?

ANNA: 'Use Head Girl for that well-groomed look'.

ALL (*sardonic*): 'Well-groomed'. Ha, ha!

A horn sounds offstage. ALL *look.*

HANS: Oh, no! That's all we need!

Enter BOBBIE *and* BILLIE, *dressed as before but with tartan additions.*

BOBBIE ⎫
BILLIE ⎭ : Hi, folks!

PEASANTS (*glum*): Hi.

BOBBIE: We're back from Edinburg!

BILLIE: And you'll never guess our problem.

PEASANTS: And you'll never guess ours!

BILLIE (*gesturing to the two of them*): This is all we have!

BOBBIE: That's right: all we stand up in!

ADAM: What do you mean?

BOBBIE: A coach-load of us have toured the whole U.K.. Am I right, Billie?

BILLIE: You're right, Bobbie.

BOBBIE: We've just returned from Bonnie Scotland, right? And we're on our way to the airport. Then what, Billie?

BILLIE: The coach bursts into flames!

BOBBIE: We've lost everything except our clothes.

BILLIE: And our money.

BOBBIE: Everything except our clothes and our money.

PEASANTS: That's terrible!

BOBBIE: All the gifts we'd bought for the folks back home: burnt! Gone!

BILLIE: We've got another coach, but where can we get another load of souvenirs?

PEASANTS: Where?

Their faces light up and they turn to look at the trolley, then they turn back to face BILLIE *and* BOBBIE, *smiling broadly.*

HANS: Right here!

BILLIE
BOBBIE } : What?

HANS: Right here! Grab those bottles, everybody!

The PEASANTS *quickly grab bottles and stand in three groups.*

HANS: We can offer you top British products like (*Gesturing*) Loyalty!

LOYALTY SINGERS: One fine day the Prince was crowned –
We saw the Coronation,
And we were filled with Loyalty
For the rulers of our nation!

HANS: And Cheer!

CHEER SINGERS: You've all seen it advertised:
The drink that tastes of paradise,
    The drink that's known as Cheer.
Why not march into the bar
Where the biggest boozers are
    And ask for a pint of Cheer?

HANS: And Head Girl!

HEAD GIRL SINGERS: Head Girl makes me radiant!
There's magic in that bottle so green!
My hair's my crowning glory
And my life's a fairy story
And people say I must be a queen!

HANS: Instant delivery of these popular brands for everyone on your coach, plus . . .

PEASANTS: Plus!

HANS: Free flags with every set of bottles!

PEASANTS (*showing flags*): Free flags!

BILLIE
BOBBIE } : Free flags! Wow!

ADAM: So how many bottles would you like?

BILLIE
BOBBIE } (*looking at each other, then nodding*): The lot!

PEASANTS: The lot?

BILLIE
BOBBIE } : That's right! How much?

HANS
ADAM } : Er, how much?

NORA: One hundred.

JANE: Two hundred.

ANNA: Three hundred.

LILY: Four hundred!

MARY: Five hundred!

PEASANTS: Five hundred pounds!

BILLIE
BOBBIE } : Is that all?

PEASANTS: That's all!

BILLIE
BOBBIE } (*counting out £100 notes*): One hundred, two hundred, three hundred, four hundred, five hundred pounds!

The coach horn sounds a long blast.

BOBBIE
BILLIE } : Coming! Wait for us!

They hurry out pushing the trolley and shouting 'Bye!

PEASANTS (*waving*): 'Bye! Have a good flight!

HANS (*holding up the money*): Five hundred pounds!

Enter COUNCILLOR PURSLOVE.

COUNCILLOR (*marching up to* HANS): Five hundred pounds! Thank you! (*Snatching the money and putting it in his briefcase*)

MARY: That's our money!

PEASANTS: Yes!

COUNCILLOR: It was yours, but it's the exact sum that you owe the council for a month's rent, *plus* your contribution towards piping water into your homes.

LILY: We're going to have piped water!

PEASANTS: Hurray!

WYNN: Five cheers for Councillor Purslove for solving all our problems!

JESS: Hold on, hold on! We still have problems! Where's the money for food?

JUDE: And our rents after this month?

MARY: I know! I've got it!

PEASANTS: What?

MARY: We'll bottle the water from the old well and sell it, like we've done to these Americans!

ANNA: Yes! Set up our own firm! A co-operative!

MIKE: The Pantoville People's Water Company!

PEASANTS: Pantoville Water! Yes!

DICK (*who has just entered unobserved with* FELICITY, *or appearing with her from the well*): I'm afraid this is our well!

PEASANTS: Yours?

JACK: Since when?

DICK: Since this morning, when Whittington Water Enterprises bought it from the council.

COUNCILLOR (*smiling smugly*): That is correct.

PEASANTS (*depressed*): Aw!

MARY: So we can't sell the water?

FELICITY: Of course not: it's ours now.

ADAM: So we've still no jobs, have we?

PEASANTS: No.

DICK: Unless you'd like to work for us.

JANE: Doing what?

FELICITY: Bottling, labelling and packing our well-known
brands: Cheer, Loyalty and Head Girl.

DICK: As advertised on T.V..

WYNN: You mean, filling bottles with water?

FELICITY: Filling them with very special water from this very
special well.

DICK: Do you want to work for us?

JESS: How much are you offering?

DICK: The minimum.

JUDE: The minimum! Wait a minute . . .

DICK: And we don't hire troublemakers!

FELICITY: You're not a troublemaker, are you?

JUDE *stands silent.*

PHIL: No, he's not, sir. Honest.

DICK: We'll be watching all of you. Start on Monday: all right?

PEASANTS (*sighing*): All right.

COUNCILLOR (*shaking hands with* DICK *and* FELICITY): On
behalf of the council, thank you both for bringing employment
to this stricken community! Goodbye!

FELICITY
DICK } : Goodbye, Councillor!

Exit COUNCILLOR PURSLOVE. *The* PEASANTS *look
depressed.*

LILY: Excuse me, shall we get new clothes when we work for
you?

FELICITY: Oh, no! We love these old-world costumes: they're so
cheerful!

DICK: That's right! Stand tall: shoulders back!

FELICITY: And smile!

DICK: This is going to be a happy firm, where we sing as we
work!

FELICITY: Yes! Do you know 'The Land of Pantomime'?

PEASANTS (*glum*): Yes, we know it!

FELICITY: Super! Let's all sing together! And don't let those smiles slip! A-one! A-two!

Smiling broadly, ALL *sing, with* DICK *and* FELICITY *in the centre.*

The Land of Pantomime

The sun is shining in the blue, the birds are singing in the trees,
The flowers in the garden are blowing in the breeze.
The windmill sails are turning and the merry churchbells chime,
And life is grand throughout the land, the land of Pantomime.

It never snows, it never rains, the weather's always bright,
There's no litter or graffiti, and everyone's polite.
We may be short of money, but we've never heard of crime,
And dreams come true for you and you (*gesturing to* DICK *and*
    FELICITY) in the land of Pantomime.

So, our hearts are full of merriment, a smile on every face:
We love to sing, we love to dance: we're happy in our place.
It's so pleasant being a peasant that we never want to climb
Any higher up the ladder in the land of Pantomime!

(*Curtain*)

OTHER TITLES IN THE SERIES

JUST LIKE US
BILL TORDOFF

Four short plays easily read or performed in one lesson with parts for the whole class.

Three are comedies. In **Classjack** a class conspire to protect their unpunctual but popular young teacher. **New World** offers a lighthearted history of Spanish 'inventions', including package holidays. In **After 'Astings** the English serfs of 1066 wrestle with the ways of their new rulers.

Just Like Us strikes a slightly more serious note, exploring racism and prejudice through the experiences of Jewish evacuees in rural England in the second world war.

Written by an experienced drama teacher, they will enable everyone to have a go and enjoy play reading.

ISBN 0 435 23902 3

LAUGHTER LINES
BILL TORDOFF

Four short comedies with parts for a whole class.

Crime Wave brings the Noah's Ark story into the present day; **The Mystery Gift** is a Trojan surprise; **2B** or **Not 2B** turns a classroom into an Arthurian castle and **Tap Tap** is a Yorkshire treasure hunt.

Specially written by an experienced drama teacher for easy acting or reading aloud in class, all four plays are above all meant to be enjoyed.

ISBN 0 435 23901 5

PLAY IT FOR LAUGHS
BILL TORDOFF

Five comedies with parts for a whole class.

With something for everyone these plays are a must for Tordoff fans!

ISBN 0 435 23900 7

THE TV SCRIPT OF
THE TURBULENT TERM OF TYKE TILER
GENE KEMP
ADAPTED BY RICHARD CALLANAN

Tyke and Danny have an all-too-eventful final term at Cricklepit
Combined School ... their final escapade almost ends in disaster.

'Devastatingly accurate and funny picture of school life and one child's
attempt to beat the system'. *The Good Book Guide to Children's Books*

Now the adventures of Tyke, Danny, Sir, Mrs Somers, Kneeshaw and
all the other favourite characters are in script form for reading and
acting in the classroom.

This TV dramatisation of Gene Kemp's popular novel is in eight five-
minute episodes ideal for reading and discussion in manageable
sections, with questions and activities with every episode.

ISBN 0 435 23003 4